STUDENT DRAMA SERIES
General Editor: MICHAEL MARLAND, B.A.

WORTH A
HEARING

TITLES IN THE SERIES

WORTH A HEARING

A COLLECTION OF RADIO PLAYS

COMPILED BY ALFRED BRADLEY

SENIOR DRAMA PRODUCER
B.B.C. NORTH REGION

With a contribution and questions by MICHAEL MARLAND, B.A.
DIRECTOR OF STUDIES
CROWN WOODS SCHOOL
LONDON

BLACKIE *LONDON & GLASGOW*

Blackie & Son Limited
BISHOPBRIGGS, GLASGOW
5 FITZHARDINGE STREET
PORTMAN SQUARE
LONDON W.1
Blackie & Son (India) Limited
103-5 FORT STREET, BOMBAY

FIRST PUBLISHED 1967

PRINTED IN GREAT BRITAIN BY BELL AND BAIN LTD.,
GLASGOW

 CONTENTS

ACKNOWLEDGMENTS

The compiler is grateful to the following for their help in the preparation of this volume:

Margaret Ramsay Limited and Mr. Plater for *The Mating Season* by Alan Plater.

A. D. Peters & Co. and Mr. Mortimer for *The Dock Brief* by John Mortimer.

Actac (Theatrical and Cinematic) Limited and Mr. Campton for *Don't Wait For Me* by David Campton.

A. D. Peters & Co. and Mr. Naughton for *She'll Make Trouble* by Bill Naughton.

Margaret Ramsay Limited and Mr. Livings for *The Day Dumbfounded Got His Pylon* by Henry Livings.

INTRODUCTION

There is an old story, popular with Radio Producers, about the small boy who said that he preferred plays on radio because the scenery was so much better. It is true that radio drama no longer commands huge audiences, but it still pleases millions of people who are willing to make an effort to participate, and many of them prefer the plays which are partly created inside their own heads.

Freed from scenery and the physical appearance of the actors, the listener is almost as close to the writer as if he were reading the play in print. For this reason, good radio plays such as *The Dark Tower*, *Under Milk Wood* or *All That Fall* have a way of echoing in the mind long after television and stage plays have been forgotten.

About seven hundred plays are broadcast by the BBC each year and although many of them are adaptations of stage plays or novels, a good proportion are written specially for radio. It is interesting that many plays, originally written to be seen in the theatre or on television, translate very easily, needing only a few simple signposts to establish the period and place. Of course, the traffic doesn't flow in only one direction and many radio plays have been adapted for films or television. Some of our best known younger generation playwrights, like Harold Pinter and Alun Owen, wrote their first work for radio, where they learned an important part of their craft—to use words effectively. There is no doubt that radio is still an important medium for the aspiring dramatist.

The Radio Producer has the job of creating a picture using only words, sound effects and music. Like any other Producer, he must always be on his guard to ensure that he is carrying out the intentions of the author. It is all too easy to get carried away by a series of brilliant sound effects without noticing that they are not adding anything important and may, in fact, be blurring the point which the author is trying to make. Sometimes, scripts by inexperienced authors are cluttered with elaborate sound effects and technical directions and it is important to remember that, however much the use of contrasting acoustics and effects may add to the interest of a play, the listeners are mainly concerned with the characters and the things they say and do. No amount of embroidery will disguise the fact that a play is lacking in substance or that the author has not thought about his characters enough. A writer who wants to make an impression in radio must have a good ear for dialogue, if he does not, the people in his play will all speak with the same voice and will refuse to come to life. He must also be able to hold the attention of the listener right from the beginning; people may be hypnotized by television, or stay in the cinema because they have paid for a seat, but if a radio play does not catch the ears of the audience in the first few minutes, it is likely to be switched off.

When you first look at the plays in this volume, some of them may seem under-written compared with stage plays, but the microphone can bring a voice so close that a soliloquy sounds as if it is being thought rather than spoken, and the writer, producer and actor have to be constantly aware of the dangers of giving a theatrical performance. Radio shows up inflated dialogue and 'ham' acting very quickly.

A radio actor has to be able to project his personality and create a character without using make-up or costume, and without the help of his body, or any facial expression. He needs a flexible voice if he is to sustain the listener's interest for an hour or more and he has to know also how to use the microphone so that he can give an impression of running, driving a car, eating or embracing, whilst, in fact, he is standing still and holding a script in his hand. A radio play is rehearsed usually for several days, during which the actors, producer and author discuss the characters, while the studio managers sort out the effects which are produced either on the spot in the studio or with the help of gramophone records and tape recordings. Gradually the elements of the play are brought together, the different sounds are blended in the control cubicle, and, as the play develops, every member of the team has to be prepared to adapt his ideas and make changes. Any play with a well-chosen cast should grow during rehearsals; if it doesn't, there is something wrong with the play—or the producer.

These five plays have two things in common. They were all written with radio in mind and they have been chosen because they deal with the world we live in today. Several of them are set in the North of England where there has been an upsurge of creative writing in recent years.

The texts are almost identical with the original radio scripts, but the studio directions have been simplified so that they can be easily read in the classroom. At the same time, the sound effects are easily recognizable if it is decided to produce them as radio plays. Despite the complex and expensive equipment of a modern broadcasting studio, a great deal can be achieved using a school tape recorder. With a little patience and ingenuity it should be possible to create all of the effects in this volume without difficulty. For more details see Mr. Marland's note at the end of the book on Producing Sound Drama in Schools. For those who want to study the technical side in depth, there is an excellent book by Alec Nisbett, *The Technique of the Sound Studio* (Focal Press), and, for a special study of writing and producing, *The Art of Radio* by Donald McWhinnie (Faber).

Although these plays were written for radio, some of them have already been performed on the stage, and all of them could easily be produced 'In-the-Round'. This is a particularly flexible form of staging which needs no platform, lighting or curtains, and has the virtue of directness and simplicity. Stephen Joseph's *Theatre in the Round* (Barrie and Rockliff) gives a clear idea of how they could be performed in a classroom or on the main floor of the school hall with very little in the way of scenery or properties.

A last word. If you decide to try your hand at writing a play, remember that well-drawn characters are much more important than sound effects, and that a story based on a nightmare, a visit to the dentist or a problem that you have faced a home or at school will probably work out better than a 'Whodunnit?' or anything else which you have not experienced at first hand.

ALFRED BRADLEY

The Mating Season

by Alan Plater

Cast:

STAN HARGREAVES

HIS MOTHER

HIS FATHER

JACK

DORIS

EILEEN

A BARMAN

The Mating Season

1 MRS. HARGREAVES. Hey, you Stan, are you going to drink your tea?

2 STAN. You what?

3 MRS. HARGREAVES. Your tea. It's getting cold, do you want it?

4 STAN. I don't know . . .

5 MRS. HARGREAVES. Well, I don't know, you'll have to tell me.

6 STAN. No. No, I don't think I want it.

7 MRS. HARGREAVES. Well, I asked you whether you wanted another cup and you said yes.

8 MR. HARGREAVES. He doesn't know, he doesn't listen half the time.

9 STAN. When you asked me I thought I did, but now I've changed my mind, does it matter?

10 MR. HARGREAVES. If you offered him paraffin he'd say 'Yes', he's always in a flipping dream.

11 MRS. HARGREAVES. It's just so's I know whether to clear your cup away or not, that's all.

12 STAN. There's no hurry, can't you leave them for a bit, have a sit down, get warm . . .

13 MRS. HARGREAVES. You know I can't settle when there's dirty pots on the table . . .

14 MR. HARGREAVES. If he had 'owt about him he'd help you, instead of just sitting there . . .

15 STAN. For crying out loud.

16 MRS. HARGREAVES. It's all right, I can manage . . .

17 MR. HARGREAVES. You get stuck in that chair, it'd take dynamite to shift you . . .

1 STAN. Well I don't see you rushing to help, any road . . .

2 MR. HARGREAVES. I'm busy.

   Pause.

3 STAN. Busy?

4 MR. HARGREAVES. I'm checking my pools.

5 MRS. HARGREAVES. I'll just take these pots through.

   She goes off to the kitchen.

6 STAN. Parliament is in session. Mr. Hargreaves said 'Winning all this money will not alter my way of life and I'll be at work first thing in the morning, the same as usual...'

   MR. HARGREAVES *tears up the coupon.*

7 STAN. When are we moving into the higher income group then, Dad?

8 MR. HARGREAVES. United!

9 STAN. United!

10 MR. HARGREAVES. That's who let me down.

11 STAN. Serves you right, putting them on your coupon.

12 MR. HARGREAVES. It's that manager.

13 STAN. They should be playing in blooming Church League.

14 MR. HARGREAVES. That's the trouble, it's that manager.

15 STAN. How many did they lose by?

16 MR. HARGREAVES. They didn't, they damn well won . . .

17 STAN. Well, what can you expect, I'd have thought you'd have more sense.

18 MR. HARGREAVES. I'd like to see you do any better, seeing as you know it all . . .

19 MRS. HARGREAVES [*returning from the kitchen*]. Did we win then, Dad?

20 STAN. I don't think he wants to talk about it.

4

1 MRS. HARGREAVES. Oh well, never mind, it's a good night on telly. Switch on, Stan.

2 STAN. Do we have to have telly on?

3 MR. HARGREAVES. You know your mother likes George Dixon.

4 STAN. I can't read with that thing blaring away.

5 MRS. HARGREAVES. Go on, it'll be starting.

6 MR. HARGREAVES. You want to start thinking about what other people want, for a change . . .

7 STAN. Well you just sit here, night after night, stagnating in front of that thing. You want to get out of the rut, go out somewhere.

8 MR. HARGREAVES. What? To the pictures?

9 MRS. HARGREAVES. Mind out, Dad, I'll switch it on. You'll still be arguing the toss when flipping Epilogue comes on . . .

10 MR. HARGREAVES. It's his fault, he's in one of his dreams again . . .

11 MRS. HARGREAVES. Are you off out tonight then, Stan?

12 STAN. Doesn't look like it, does it?

13 MRS. HARGREAVES. Thought you might, with it being Saturday like.

14 STAN. Thought I'd stop in.

15 MRS. HARGREAVES. I mean, Saturday night, you were never in, were you?

16 STAN. I'm stopping in. I'm having a bit of a read.

17 MR. HARGREAVES. Well, it beats me, it does, honest.

18 STAN. What's the matter?

19 MR. HARGREAVES. When I was your age, I used to read books.

20 STAN. What about it? Lots of people read books. They have libraries and that . . .

21 MR. HARGREAVES. You're always reading gramophone records.

5

1　STAN. I'm not always reading gramophone records.

2　MR. HARGREAVES. Every time I look at you you're stuck behind one of them things.

3　MRS. HARGREAVES. He can read what he likes, Dad, if he wants to read gramophone records, that's all right . . .

4　STAN [*losing patience*]. I am not reading flipping gramophone records. This is what is called the sleeve, it tells you all about the artist and the music and that . . .

5　MR. HARGREAVES. Making excuses for it, more like . . .

6　STAN. Look, you can learn a lot reading these things. I mean, what do you know about Dave Brubeck? Go on, let's hear it . . .

7　MR. HARGREAVES. Doesn't he play left-half for Stockport County?

8　STAN. Does he heck as like, he plays the blooming piano . . .

9　MRS. HARGREAVES. Do you mind, I can't hear a thing for the two of you and I'm trying to watch . . .

　　Pause.

10　MR. HARGREAVES. It's his fault, he's reading gramophone records.

11　STAN. Oh 'ell, I've had enough of this, I'm going upstairs . . .

12　MRS. HARGREAVES. Aye, well, maybe we'll get a bit of peace . . .

13　MR. HARGREAVES. And don't go playing that thing full blast, we'll have the neighbours in again . . .

14　STAN. You won't hear 'owt, you'll be hard on in five minutes . . . [*He moves to the door.*]

15　MR. HARGREAVES. Oh, go to . . .

16　MRS. HARGREAVES. Now then, Dad.

　　STAN *closes the door behind him.*

17　MRS. HARGREAVES. You're a right pair, you two. You're as bad as he is. Mind you, it's not natural, him going off to his room every night, he should be off out, lad of his age . . .

1   MR. HARGREAVES. You don't want to waste your time worrying about him.

2   MRS. HARGREAVES. It's only since Jack got married, he hasn't got a mate to go around with now . . .

3   MR. HARGREAVES. Well, that's it, what do you expect? Nobody'll go out with him, you can't blame them . . .

4   MRS. HARGREAVES. But Saturday night, you'd expect him to go out Saturday night . . .

5   MR. HARGREAVES. He wants a good shaking up, that's what he wants, always in a flipping dream . . . [*Yawns.*] Hot, this fire, makes you feel a bit dozy . . .

Fade out.

A few moments later. STAN *is brooding in his bedroom.*

6   STAN [*sighing*]. Well, here we are again. Welcome to Saturday night at home with Stanley Hargreaves. Starring your favourite D.J., playing records to himself cause he's nowt better to do. Dave Brubeck playing left-half for Stockport flipping County! Blimey, if Dad had his way he'd have the Coldstream Guards and the Archbishop of Canterbury and the Cabinet all dressed in striped jerseys with numbers on the back. Let's have some music. The food of you know what.

He plays a Frank Sinatra record.

Marvellous! Reading gramophone records. Dad probably thinks that when anyone dies, it's because so all-powerful celestial bloke in black shorts blows a whistle. He wants a good shaking up, that's his trouble. Wants to listen to a bit of good music. [*He sings, rather badly, with the record.*] You know, Stan, you're a bit like Sinatra yourself. Here, have a look in the mirror. Yes. That's it. Tie hanging loose, collar undone, cigarette sort of dangling, tough like. Stick the old Robin Hood on the back of your head. Suck in a bit, make your

cheeks go hollow. Yes. [*Impressed. Sings a few more bars.*] Oh
Hell! You want locking up.

He switches the record-player off.

Saturday night! Stuck here on your jack. Jack? [*Laughs.*]
Yes, that's it. It was all right before Jack got married, we
had some smashing times, me and Jack. I don't know,
he seemed to be able to enjoy himself somehow,
without trying. I mean, he wouldn't be doing this, in
my position. He'd be with it. He'd know what to do. I
wonder what he'd say . . .

2 JACK [*his voice should have slight echo effect to distinguish from reality*].
He'd say you're a big nelly.

3 STAN. You what?

4 JACK. You're a big nelly.

5 STAN. Who you calling a nelly?

6 JACK. Well I mean, Saturday night and you're sitting here
rotting away . . .

7 STAN. I'm developing a deeper appreciation of music . . .

8 JACK. On Saturday night? Don't give me that.

9 STAN. Straight up.

10 JACK. You can develop a deeper appreciation of all sorts of
things on Saturday night, but music isn't one of them.
Except down the Palais . . .

11 STAN. Oh, I don't know . . .

12 JACK. And you don't go down the Palais to listen to the
music . . .

13 STAN. All right, all right, so what should I do?

14 JACK. You want to get out and enjoy yourself. Find yourself
a nice bit of crumpet . . .

15 STAN. I might have known you'd suggest that.

16 JACK. Well, what's wrong with it? Simple human, basic,
fundamental, flaming psychology. Man and Woman.
Didn't your old man tell you about it?

1 STAN. All he taught me was the offside rule.

2 JACK. Well, come on then.

3 STAN. Come on what?

4 JACK. Get smartened up a bit. You can't go out looking like a slob.

5 STAN. No, I don't think I'll go out. Got a bit of headache . . .

6 JACK. You heard.

7 STAN. It's the weather, it's been sort of humid all day . . .

8 JACK. Where's your tie?

9 STAN. There's one there, hanging on the chair.

10 JACK. It looks like a bit of chewed cardboard. Haven't you got another one?

11 STAN. There's this one, sort of Slim Jim, I don't like it much.

12 JACK. It's the best you've got by the looks of things. How about a wash?

13 STAN. I had one at dinner-time.

14 JACK. You wouldn't consider having another one?

15 STAN. Er . . . No, I don't think so. Keep it informal. [*Pause.*] Hey, I didn't say I was going out. I've got a headache.

16 JACK. You want shaking up a bit, you're in a rut, Stan.

17 STAN. I'm all right, honest, I enjoy a quiet evening by myself.

18 JACK. Well, you've put your tie on now, haven't you?

19 STAN. Yes, I have.

20 JACK. Well then. You can wear your Robin Hood as well.

21 STAN. What, that thing? Makes me look a right nana.

22 JACK. Rubbish!

23 STAN. No, look, Jack, it makes me look a proper Herbert.

24 JACK. You've got a blooming complex, mate. I'll tell you something. When you're standing there like that, with your tie hanging loose, and your collar button undone, and the old fag dangling, I'd say it gave you the Sinatra look . . .

25 STAN. Getaway.

1 JACK. **Straight up, Stan.** Not handsome, exactly, but sort of worldly.

2 STAN. Bit cynical?

3 JACK. Yes, just a bit. You've been around a bit.

4 STAN. If I . . . er . . . sort of suck in, I can make my cheeks go hollow. Does that make it better?

5 JACK. Yes, you do that, Stan, you do that. It suits you.

6 STAN. Oh well, we'll be off then.

    Pause.

7 JACK. Where are you going?

8 STAN. Yes. Yes. I hadn't thought of that.

9 JACK. All dressed up and nowhere to go . . .

10 STAN. Can't you think of something?

11 JACK. You want to buy a paper, go down the 'Grapes', have a few jars and see what's on. Wherever you go, you want tanking up first.

12 STAN. That's true. If I get a bit of ale in, it'll stop me thinking about my hat. Yes, that's it. I'll go down the 'Grapes'. Better tell them I'm off out.

    He walks down the stairs, and opens the door.

13 STAN. It's only me. I'm off out.

14 MRS. HARGREAVES. I thought you were staying in.

15 STAN. Aye, well, I changed my mind. I just thought I'd go out

16 MR. HARGREAVES [*dozily*]. What's he up to now?

17 MRS. HARGREAVES. He's off out.

18 MR. HARGREAVES. What? Dressed up like that?

19 STAN. What's the matter with it?

20 MR. HARGREAVES. With that daft hat on? You want locking up.

21 STAN. Well I'm going, anyhow. See you later.

1   MRS. HARGREAVES. Tata then, love. Don't be too late.
      STAN *closes the door.*

2   MR. HARGREAVES. I never seen 'owt like it in my life.

3   MRS. HARGREAVES. I know, he wants locking up, now shut up.

4   MR. HARGREAVES [*yawns*]. I think I'll just have five minutes.

    Fade out.

Fade in the background noise of a public house. It is fairly quiet.

5   STAN. Half a bitter, please.

6   BARMAN. Half of bitter.

7   STAN. Ta.

8   BARMAN. Ta.

    Pause.

9   BARMAN [*trying to establish some sort of contact*]. Aye well.

10 STAN. Yes.

11 BARMAN. Still the same out?

12 STAN. Just about.

13 BARMAN. Has been for a bit.

14 STAN. Too long.

15 BARMAN. Bad for colds.

    Pause.

    You haven't been in for a bit, have you?

16 STAN. No, not for a bit.

17 BARMAN. Thought you hadn't.

18 STAN. I used to come in with a pal of mine.

19 BARMAN. Aye. Aye, I remember. Ginger hair.

20 STAN. That's right.

    Pause.

21 BARMAN. He hasn't been in for a bit.

1 STAN. He got married.

2 BARMAN. Oh, well he won't will he?

3 STAN. I shouldn't think so.

4 BARMAN. I mean, if I was married, I wouldn't come here.

5 STAN. Don't suppose I would, either.

6 BARMAN. Course I work here so it's a bit different, isn't it? [*He laughs uneasily.*]

7 STAN. Aye, it's a bit different.

   Pause.

8 BARMAN. I'd been wondering why he hadn't been in.

9 STAN. He doesn't come now.

10 BARMAN. Mind you, it's a bit since you were in, isn't it?

11 STAN. Aye, it's a fair while.

12 BARMAN. I thought so.

13 STAN. This mate of mine, he got married.

14 BARMAN. Oh aye, that's right, someone was telling me . . .

   Pause.

   Still the same out?

15 STAN. Just about.

16 BARMAN. Has been for a bit. Bad for colds.

17 STAN [*giving up*]. I'll go and sit down, I think, read my paper.

18 BARMAN. Aye well.

   Pause.

19 STAN. Well, Jack, I'm having a riotous time.

20 JACK. You'll be all right when you've had a drop of ale. What you supping halves for?

21 STAN. Bit out of practice.

22 JACK. You're running to seed. Have a look in your paper, see what's on.

1 STAN. Hey, Jack, are you still there? You see that fellow in the corner?

2 JACK. What about him?

3 STAN. I think he's looking at my hat.

4 JACK. Don't be daft. It's that fellow sells papers down the road. He always looks gormless like that. Right twit. Have a look at your paper.

5 STAN. Now then. There's the Odeon. 'I Was a Teenage Werewolf' and 'The Thing From a Thousand Fathoms'!

6 JACK. Kid's stuff. 'Owt else?

7 STAN. Few war films.

8 JACK. 'The Valiant Years' and that . . .

9 STAN. Some of them are all right.

10 JACK. See one, you've seen the lot. They're just making the Germans a bit nicer now, seeing as how we're friends, you know, NATO all that stuff . . .

11 STAN. What about the Continental?

12 JACK. You mean where they have those mucky foreign pictures?

13 STAN. Nights in Paris, a tour of Parisian night spots, with English sub-titles . . .

14 JACK. Sub-titles, yes, I know. You get this sexy French piece jabbering away for about three flipping weeks and then all it says down the bottom is 'No'. Waste of time.

15 STAN. What about the wrestling? . . . I'm sure he's looking at my hat.

16 JACK. He isn't looking at your hat.

7 STAN. I'll thump his lug if he is.

18 JACK. What about the wrestling?

19 STAN. Oh aye, the wrestling. Abdul, the Butcher of Bagdad versus the Masked Vampire . . .

20 JACK. Will the Vampire lose his undefeated record and have to remove his mask, thus revealing the secret of his identity? I doubt it.

1 STAN. How do you know?

2 JACK. He never does. Anyhow, if you want to know who it is, it's Len Cartwright, plays prop. forward for Trinity. You know, he got sent off in the semi-final last year, the big nut.

3 STAN. He's the Vampire?

4 JACK. Can't play Rugby, like, he just likes a punch-up.

5 STAN. All right, so if the wrestling's no good, and there's nothing on at the pictures, where am I going to go?

6 JACK. You know damn well where you're going.

Pause.

7 STAN. The Palais?

8 JACK. The Palais.

9 STAN. On my own?

10 JACK. There's dozens of pretty little girls just waiting for a lad like you.

11 STAN. Are you sure?

12 JACK. Course I'm sure.

13 STAN. If he doesn't stop looking at my hat I'll have him. So help me, I'll have him.

14 JACK. Have another beer, forget about your blooming hat.

15 STAN. Well, it's all right, but it's not on . . . well is it?

No reply.

Better have another, I suppose. Same again, please. No, make it a pint this time.

16 BARMAN. Make it a pint.

17 STAN. Ta.

18 BARMAN. Ta.

Pause.

Aye well. Off out then?

1 STAN. Might just pop in the Palais.
2 BARMAN. Lot of them go there.
3 STAN. Just for a look round, like.
4 BARMAN. Aye.

   Pause.

5 STAN. Haven't been for a bit, like.
6 BARMAN. Well, you haven't been in here for a bit, have
   you?
7 STAN. No.
8 BARMAN. Still the same out, fellow was saying.
9 STAN. Has been for a bit.
10 BARMAN. Still, you've got your hat on.
11 STAN [*slightly aggressive*]. You what?
12 BARMAN. Aye well.

   Pause.

   Course, you might just meet her.
13 STAN. Who?
14 BARMAN [*with slight sarcasm*]. Girl of your dreams.
15 STAN. Girl of my dreams?
16 BARMAN. Down the Palais.
17 STAN. I haven't been for a bit.
18 BARMAN. You never know. She might be waiting.
19 STAN. Aye.
20 BARMAN. What happened to that pal of yours? He hasn't
   been in for a bit.

   Fade out.

Fade in on the dance hall. The band is playing a lively quickstep.

21 DORIS. You don't half smell of beer.
22 STAN. You what?
23 DORIS. Well, it's not very nice, is it? You wouldn't like it.

1 STAN. I think it's marvellous.

2 DORIS. Well, it's all right for you.

3 STAN. I'm sorry.

4 DORIS. It's like dancing in a brewery.

5 STAN. I said I'm sorry.

6 DORIS. I mean, how would you like it if all the girls you danced with smelled of brown ale?

7 STAN. It isn't brown ale, it's best bitter. [*Pause.*] What do you come for if you don't like it?

8 DORIS. Mandy likes to come.

9 STAN. Mandy? [*Pause.*] Who's Mandy?

10 DORIS. She's my friend.

11 STAN. You're with your friend then?

12 DORIS. Well, you can't come here by yourself, can you?

13 STAN. I don't see why not.

14 DORIS. Don't you read the papers?

15 STAN. Course I read the papers.

16 DORIS. Well. They're full of it.

17 STAN. What?

18 DORIS. Well, you know.

Pause.

That sort of thing.

19 STAN. Oh aye.

Pause.

20 DORIS. You don't jive then?

21 STAN. No, I don't jive.

22 DORIS. Makes you feel a bit soft.

23 STAN. What does?

24 DORIS. When everybody else is jiving, and you doing slow, slow, quick, quick, slow.

25 STAN. Well, you're not forced to jive.

16

1   DORIS. You feel so soft.

2   STAN. There's no law saying you've got to jive.

3   DORIS. I know that, but . . .

4   STAN. I mean, there's no notices up saying 'Thou shalt jive'.

     Pause.

5   DORIS. When you asked me for the dance I thought you meant jiving . . .

6   STAN. Oh, all right then, if you don't like it, we'll pack it in I'm sorry you've been troubled.

7   DORIS. Well, you feel so soft . . .

     Pause.

8   STAN. Would you like a cup of coffee or something?

9   DORIS. I'll have to look for Mandy.

10   STAN. Oh aye, that's right, you're with your friend.

11   DORIS. There she is, yoo-hoo, Mandy! There, she's seen me.

12   STAN. Oh, that's Mandy.

13   DORIS. Bonny, isn't she? Real shy, you know . . .

14   STAN. Well, I'll be off then. Thank you for the dance . . .

15   DORIS. Hello, love . . . hey, I thought you were taking us for a cup of coffee . . .

16   STAN. I've just remembered . . . telephone call I've got to make, sorry. I'll see you later on, maybe . . .

17   DORIS. Well! You meet some funny types here . . . are you having a good time, Mandy? [*She moves off in search of better company.*]

18   STAN. It's no good, Jack, you shouldn't have made me come. [*Mimicking.*] Don't you jive then?

19   JACK. Well, don't you?

20   STAN. Not when I've been supping. Makes it swill about too much. Nice gentle waltz, something like that, that's more like it. Oh Hell, it's Latin-American now, that's no good . . .

1 JACK. Can't you do that, either?

2 STAN. Heck, don't you remember that time I did the Samba, that time I fell over. You know, that rugby union club dance, when we got chucked out for laughing at the band.

3 JACK. Yes, I remember. But it's no time for reminiscences. You want to be getting yourself organized. Have a look round, see what sort of a field we've got.

4 STAN. There's plenty of time.

5 JACK. Is there heck as like! You know what happens. Old Hotlips Ferguson announces the next dance, and by the time you wake up all the best stuff's gone. You get stuck with the fat ones, the faded ones and them with glasses.

6 STAN. Like Mandy.

7 JACK. Yes, like Mandy. Get doing some research. Now, let's see. What about that little blonde piece there, dancing with the bloke in the wedding suit?

8 STAN. He looks a bit old for her.

9 JACK. It's Harry Potter, runs the beginners' class on Mondays. He'll be trying to sign her on for the formation dancing team.

10 STAN. Or something.

11 JACK. Or something.

12 STAN. Yes, she's all right.

13 JACK. Well try to work up a bit of enthusiasm. She's all right. She's more than all right, She's got a bit of class.

14 STAN. What if she's with a friend?

15 JACK. Now look. When the music stops, don't let her out of your sight. Then when they announce the next dance, pounce. Don't mess about.

16 STAN. He's asking her something, look.

17 JACK. You're all right, she's shaking her head.

18 STAN. Maybe she doesn't like formation dancing.

1 JACK. O.K., we'll just go over the drill again. What's the first thing you do?

2 STAN. Get her talking.

3 JACK. What about?

4 STAN. About herself.

5 JACK. Right. Women all like talking about themselves. Find out where she works, then you know where to ring up. What else?

6 STAN [*a little wearily*]. Don't let her get away. Take her for a cup of coffee.

7 JACK. It's not very original, but it works. Now watch it, he's going to announce the next dance. Shirt collar undone, tie dangling, check?

8 STAN. Check.

9 JACK. Good lad.

10 STAN. Have I to do my hollow cheeks?

11 JACK. Yes, you do that.

12 STAN. Blast! It's a lady's desire . . .

13 JACK. That doesn't matter. Ask her to desire you, go on, she's just down there near the next pillar, don't mess about . . .

14 STAN. Is it all right though?

15 JACK. Get on with it, you're wasting time . . .

Pause.

16 STAN. Excuse me, I wonder if you'd like to desire me . . .

17 EILEEN. Oh, my feet are ever so tired . . .

18 STAN. Are they? Er . . .

19 JACK. Improvise, improvise . . .

20 STAN. I only dance very slowly.

21 EILEEN. All right then.

They dance to a waltz tune.

22 STAN. It's . . . er . . . crowded then.

19

1 EILEEN. Yes.

2 STAN. Suppose it's with it being Saturday . . . and that.

3 EILEEN. I expect so.

4 STAN. Long time since I've been here, don't really like it very much.

5 EILEEN. Don't you?

6 STAN. Get's a bit crowded.

7 EILEEN. Suppose it's with it being Saturday.

8 STAN. Yes. Yes, I suppose that's it.

   Pause.

9 JACK. You're breaking every rule in the book, Stan.

10 STAN. Oh, button it, can't you?

11 JACK. Well stop messing about.

   Pause.

12 STAN. What's your name then?

13 EILEEN. Eileen.

14 STAN. Oh aye. Er . . . nice name. Do you work? I mean where do you work?

15 EILEEN. Cracker works.

16 STAN. You what?

17 EILEEN. Cracker works.

18 STAN. Don't think I've heard of that.

19 EILEEN. It's a big place.

20 STAN. Yes, yes, I expect it is.

21 EILEEN [*suddenly forthcoming, suggesting she's been weighing Stan up*]. They make cream crackers and cheese biscuits and them nylon buns for slimming with.

22 STAN. Yes, my mam likes them. What do you do then?

23 EILEEN. Me?

24 STAN. Yes, what do you do? Butter them?

1   EILEEN [*laughing*]. No, I'm a private secretary.

2   STAN. What, like a typist, you mean?

3   EILEEN. No, a secretary.

4   STAN. What's the difference, then? I've often wondered.

5   EILEEN. I don't know. It just says so on my card.

6   STAN. Do you like it then?

7   EILEEN. It's not bad. Money's all right.

   Pause.

8   JACK. Hold hard, Stan.

9   STAN. Why?

10 JACK. That's enough about her for the moment. If she's going to bite, she'll ask you about you.

11 STAN. Will she?

12 JACK. Nice touch about buttering the biscuits. Always helps if you can get a laugh. Breaks the tension.

13 STAN. Thank you. I'll wait then.

   Pause.

14 EILEEN. What's your name then?

15 STAN [*without thinking*]. Funny you should say that. He said you might . . .

16 EILEEN. What you talking about?

17 STAN. Sorry. I was thinking about something else. Er . . . Stan, Stanley for short, no, the other way about. [*He is a little nervous.*]

18 EILEEN. What's the matter?

19 STAN. Nothing. Just call me Stan.

20 EILEEN. I suppose I ought to ask you where you work, if we're being polite and that. [*She knows the rules.*]

21 STAN. I'm just a clerk. Sort of low-class civil servant.

22 EILEEN. Where? Up at the Town Hall?

23 STAN. Down the Labour Exchange.

1 EILEEN. Do you like it?

2 STAN. It's lousy.

3 EILEEN. Oh.

Pause.

4 JACK. You big nit! Saying a thing like that.

5 STAN. It is lousy.

6 JACK. You don't have to tell the flaming truth. She doesn't know what to say now.

7 STAN. Sorry, Jack.

8 JACK. You're getting cocky with it, that's the trouble. You'd better try to sort it out.

Pause.

9 STAN. Mind you, we have some good fun in the office, it's just the paperwork gets a bit much sometimes.

10 EILEEN. What sort of fun?

11 STAN. Well, see, we all have a counter to look after. There's Sid on Heavy Industrial, George on Engineering, Herbert on Clerical, me on Miscellaneous. With me being the youngest, I've only been there two months, I get Miscellaneous, you see. Well, we have these competitions to see who can get the longest queue. Blimey, it's a laugh.

12 EILEEN. You mean the men just stand there and you don't bother with them?

13 STAN. They'll stand there for hours sometimes, and not a dickey-bird. Old Sid's the best of the lot, you ought to see the queues he gets . . .

14 EILEEN. Well I don't think that's very funny.

15 STAN. Don't you?

16 EILEEN. I bet the men in the queue don't laugh.

17 STAN. That's all right, they're only . . . come to think of it, they don't.

1 EILEEN. I think it's rotten.

2 STAN. Well we don't actually do it as much as we used to . . . [*Trying to retrieve the situation.*] It was Sid's idea, he's a bit twisted is Sid.

3 EILEEN. He must be.

4 STAN. Yes, he is . . . er, would you like a cup of coffee?

5 EILEEN. I don't know.

6 STAN. What do you mean, you don't know?

7 EILEEN. It's a bit difficult.

8 STAN. It's all right, I'll pay.

9 EILEEN. Do you mind waiting five minutes?

10 STAN. Five minutes? No, I don't think . . .

11 FILEEN. Well wait at the bottom of the stairs, you know where I mean, and if I don't come in five minutes I'm not coming. O.K.?

12 STAN. All right. That is, it's all right as long as you come.

13 EILEEN [*coy*]. Well, that's up to you, isn't it? [*She moves away.*]

14 STAN. Yes, all right, at the end of the dance.

15 STAN. Well, Jack?

16 JACK. So far, so good.

17 STAN. As long as she comes.

18 JACK. It's all part of the system. She'll be here in about ten minutes.

19 STAN. No, you didn't hear right, it's five minutes.

20 JACK. She's just trying you out, make sure you're interested.

21 STAN. Yes, but, I mean, what's she doing? While I'm waiting.

22 JACK. Well, you know what women are like. She'll be having a spit and a drag, combing her hair and that. Having a word with her friend.

23 STAN. No, this one hasn't got a friend.

24 JACK. They've all got friends. Don't you know anything? Very gregarious, women at dances. Hell's bells, didn't

23

you learn anything when you used to come here with me? What did you do all the time?

2 STAN. You always just disappeared, and I'd never see you again. I'd hang around for a bit then I'd go home.

3 JACK. All right, I'll explain. She'll tell her friend she's just going for a cup of coffee, right?

4 STAN. Yes.

5 JACK. And she'll make arrangements for if you take her home.

6 STAN. I never said anything about taking her home.

7 JACK. It's your next job, isn't it?

8 STAN. She might live miles away.

9 JACK. Well you can't say please may I escort you to your front door, providing it's not too far from where I live. You can't do that.

10 STAN. It's a bit dodgey though.

11 JACK. You're just bone idle, that's your trouble. This is serious, this sort of thing, you've got to work at it. She's nice, isn't she?

12 STAN. She's all right.

13 JACK. O.K. so maybe you'll have to slog it for a couple of miles afterwards, so what?

14 STAN. It's cold.

15 JACK. You've got your hat.

16 STAN. Hey, have I still got my collar undone?

17 JACK. Hollow cheeks.

18 STAN. I'll light a fag for dangling purposes.

19 JACK. Check, check, check. All ready for action. Yes, a face that has seen much suffering. How long have you been waiting now?

20 STAN. About ten minutes.

21 JACK. Should be here soon.

Pause.

1 EILEEN. Oh, hello, am I late?

2 STAN. Just a bit, but it doesn't matter.

3 EILEEN. I'm sorry.

4 STAN. Come on, there'll be a bit of a queue.

Fade out.

Fade in the juke box playing in the dance hall coffee bar.

5 STAN. There you are. I spilt most of it in the saucer but there's still a bit in the cup.

6 EILEEN. Ta, that's all right.

7 STAN. Do you want a cigarette?

8 EILEEN. I don't smoke, thanks. I can't afford it.

9 STAN. Well, I don't very much. Just at dances and that, you know, to be sociable . . . They've had this place done up since I was here last.

10 EILEEN. You can't have been for a bit.

11 STAN. Well, there was this mate of mine, I used to come with him a lot but he got married, and then I didn't have anybody to come with.

12 EILEEN. What made you come tonight?

13 STAN. I don't know really. He sort of suggested . . . I don't know, maybe it was Fate.

14 EILEEN. You what?

15 STAN. Fate. Perhaps Fate ordained that I should come here and that you should come here, and that we should meet.

Pause.

16 EILEEN. Your shirt collar's undone.

17 STAN. Oh, is it? I'll . . . er . . . fasten it then. Do you come every week then?

18 EILEEN. Sometimes.

1 STAN. I see.

Pause.

2 JACK. Watch it, Stan, you're pushing it a bit. Go a bit easier.

3 STAN. I think you're right.

4 JACK. That's door-step talk, that stuff about Fate. Tell her her hair looks nice, that's not a bad move.

Pause.

5 STAN. Your hair looks nice.

6 EILEEN. Do you think so?

7 STAN. With the lights and that shining on it. Very nice

8 EILEEN. Ta. It's natural, you know.

9 STAN. Oh aye, I realize that. Soon as I saw it, I said to myself, that hasn't come out of a bottle.

10 EILEEN. Not like that thing sitting at the next table. Look. Mind, she might see you looking. With the tight skirt on.

11 STAN. What lovely knees.

12 EILEEN. I think it's cheap and nasty.

13 STAN. Wants locking up.

14 EILEEN. She'll only be about fifteen as well.

15 STAN. She must have got rid of Mandy, any road.

16 EILEEN. You what?

17 STAN. That's her friend.

18 EILEEN. You don't mean to tell me you know her?

19 STAN [*Hastily*]. No, not really. Used to go to the same . . . er . . . Sunday school.

Pause.

20 EILEEN. What school did you go to?

21 STAN. Oh, I went to St. Mark's, passed the old scholarship like.

22 EILEEN. You must be clever.

1　STAN. Second chance, late developer.

2　EILEEN. It's a Catholic School, isn't it?

3　STAN. Yes, that's right. I mean, we're not, but we had to say which school we preferred and dad reckoned they had the best football team. Handy for the buses as well.

4　EILEEN. I went to Alderman Fairweather's up on the estate.

5　STAN. Good school, isn't it?

6　EILEEN. School's all right. It's the teachers, they're all so daft.

7　STAN. What's daft about them?

8　EILEEN. They never taught you anything. I mean, you go to school to learn things, don't you? That's the only reason. But oh no, they wanted you playing netball, and singing in choirs, and verse-speaking, you know, for the Music Festival. Spent half your time chasing up and down a field waving hockey sticks about. What good's that?

9　STAN. Don't you like music then?

10　EILEEN. Some of it's all right, not this Nymphs and Shepherds stuff.

11　STAN. Frank Sinatra?

12　EILEEN. Oh yes, I like him.

13　STAN. Just got a new L.P. of his today, haven't even played it yet.

14　EILEEN. I'd like to hear that.

15　STAN. I'll lend it if you like.

16　EILEEN. Will you? Ta.

　　　Pause.

17　JACK. Well done, Stan, you're back on the lines again now.

18　STAN. Good idea about lending her the record.

19　JACK. You want to be trying her out about taking her home soon.

20　STAN. Do you think it's warm enough?

1 JACK. There's the last waltz. Some of them like the last waltz, you know, soft lights, all that stuff, romantic like . . .

2 STAN. Still, the forecast didn't mention rain . . .

3 JACK. Anyhow, go careful, Stan, this is the first major crisis . . .

Pause.

4 EILEEN. Are you smoking again?

5 STAN. Just thought I'd have one . . .

6 EILEEN. I wish you'd smoke it properly. You look like a bookie's runner with it dangling like that.

7 STAN. It's just the way I . . .

8 EILEEN. The smoke keeps getting in my eyes . . .

9 STAN. Sorry.

10 EILEEN. Have you got something on your mind, or something?

11 STAN [*with over-casual air*]. No, no. Do you fancy strolling down for the last waltz, it'll be on soon.

12 EILEEN. Is it as late as that? I'll have to be going.

13 STAN. Couldn't we have the last waltz first before you . . .

14 EILEEN. It's my bus, there's always a queue . . .

15 STAN. You'll have to be going then?

16 EILEEN. Soon.

Pause.

17 JACK. Well, Stan?

18 STAN. Well, Jack?

19 JACK. Good luck.

20 STAN. Ta.

21 JACK. Roger and out.

Pause.

22 STAN. Can I take you home then?

1   EILEEN. There's no need for you to do that . . .
2   STAN. No, honest, I'd like to.
3   EILEEN. It's complicated, you don't understand . . .
4   STAN. No, it isn't complicated. I just want to take you home.
      That isn't complicated.
5   EILEEN. Well I can't really.
6   STAN. Oh, stone me!
7   EILEEN. We'll have to get the twenty past then.
8   STAN. Is that the last bus?
9   EILEEN. No, but . . .
10   STAN. What's wrong with the last one?
11   EILEEN. I'm going on the twenty past, are you coming?
12   STAN. Well, come on then, you'll have to get your skates
      on . . . See you at the front door.

   Fade out.

Fade in street noises outside the dance hall with occasional sounds of traffic.

13   STAN. Oh come on, hurry up, we'll miss the flaming bus.
14   JACK. You know the drill now, Stan?
15   STAN. Sorry, Jack, haven't got time to talk.
16   JACK. You've got your hat on crooked.
17   STAN. Can't help that, she's coming . . .
18   JACK. See you around then.
19   STAN. Come on, hurry up . . . the driver's getting in . . .

   Fade out.

The estate. There is the noise of the bus driving away. Their footsteps can be heard on the pavement.

20   STAN. This is where you live then?
21   EILEEN. Haven't recovered from running for that bus yet.
      Yes, just down here.

1   STAN. Nice night then.

2   EILEEN. That's a funny little hat you've got on.

3   STAN. Don't you like it?

4   EILEEN. It's different.

5   STAN. Yes . . . Yes, that's what I think.

6   EILEEN. Suits you, in a funny sort of way.

7   STAN. I'm glad.

8   EILEEN. This is our house.

9   STAN. Stone rabbits then.

10   EILEEN. My mam likes them, I think it's daft.

11   STAN. You ought to fix her up with a couple of gnomes and a wishing well, that'd settle the neighbours.

12   EILEEN. If you're going to hang around here, we'd better go in the passage. Dad'll be out with the bottles.

13   STAN. Do they deliver beer round here then?

14   EILEEN. He's a big bloke my dad.

15   STAN. Doesn't he like strangers on the estate or something?

16   EILEEN. That's what makes it complicated.

17   STAN. Oh Hell, are we on complicated again. Has he got a horsewhip?

18   EILEEN. It's all right for you; it's easy for you.

19   STAN. But you keep making things complicated.

20   EILEEN. Well, you haven't got a boy-friend in the Air Force…

21   STAN. I should think I haven't! . . . [*Truth dawning.*] You what?

22   EILEEN. I've got a boy-friend in the Air Force.

Pause. A dog howls in the distance.

23   STAN. I only hope it doesn't rain then, that's all.

24   EILEEN. Well, it's a bit rotten, isn't it?

25   STAN. Oh aye, it's rotten all right.

26   EILEEN. With him being so far away.

27   STAN. What, is he abroad or something?

1 EILEEN. He's at Padgate.

2 STAN. Padgate. Charming place. It's a picture this time of year.

3 EILEEN. What, were you there?

4 STAN. I can show you the scars.

5 EILEEN. Well, it's not really fair, is it?

6 STAN. No, it's not really fair. Are you . . . engaged, like?

7 EILEEN. Engaged?

8 STAN. Yes, you know. Rings and wedding bells, ham salad and that?

9 EILEEN. Course not. Oh, he wanted to, but I don't want to be tied down like that. I mean, once you're engaged, that's it, you can't enjoy yourself at all, can you?

10 STAN. I don't know. I've never been engaged.

11 EILEEN. Neither have I. I don't want to be, either, not yet anyway.

12 STAN. It's complicated all right.

Pause.

13 EILEEN. That's why we had to come on the twenty past. My friend gets the last bus and it's her brother. If she'd seen us, it'd be terrible. She can't keep her mouth shut about anything.

14 STAN. Let's change the subject.

15 EILEEN. All right then. I'm sorry. After you've come all this way.

16 STAN. How do I get home?

17 EILEEN. Home?

18 STAN. Where I live.

19 EILEEN. Where do you live?

20 STAN. Runnymede Villas, number seven.

21 EILEEN. Near the railway sidings?

22 STAN. Near the railway sidings.

1 EILEEN. It's a long walk, you won't get a bus now.

2 STAN. Look, I know it's a long walk, it's a Hell of a long
    walk. I just want pointing in the right direction.

3 EILEEN. Well I think your best way's the way the bus came,
    till you get to the second lot of traffic lights, take the
    short cut along the old canal bank, on to Midlothian
    Street, then keep on till you come to that pub, what is
    it called . . . ?

4 STAN. The Grapes, yes, I know my way from there, blind-
    fold.

5 EILEEN. It's an awful long way.

6 STAN. It is when she's got a boy-friend in Her Majesty's.

7 EILEEN. Well I had to tell you, didn't I?

8 STAN. Anyhow, I still think your hair looks nice.

9 EILEEN. You'd better be going.

10 STAN. Well I do.

11 EILEEN. What's the matter with your face, Stan?

12 STAN. There's nowt the matter with it . . . well, maybe not
    handsome, but . . .

13 EILEEN. Your cheeks've gone all hollow, I noticed it before
    at the dance . . .

14 STAN. Oh blimey. No. [Confused.] It's a habit I've got. I do
    it when I'm thinking. Like some people bite their nails,
    I get hollow cheeks, do you mind?

15 EILEEN. What were you thinking about?

16 STAN. Thinking what nice hair you've got, and . . . er . . .
    what nice eyes.

17 EILEEN. What colour are they?

18 STAN. How should I know, you've gone and shut them.
    Er . . . blue. Brown.

19 EILEEN. You've got a lot to learn, Stan.

   Pause.

   There, you've had your goodnight kiss. You'd better be
   off home now.

1 STAN. Brown.

2 EILEEN. Time you were going.

3 STAN. It's three miles you know . . .

A door opens, and there is a sound of milk bottles being put out.

4 VOICE. It's all right, Ma, must have been them cats again.

The door closes.

5 STAN Better be off then.

6 EILEEN. Thanks for seeing me home.

7 STAN. See you again sometime?

8 EILEEN. No. I can't.

9 STAN. Sure?

10 EILEEN. You know the way things are.

11 STAN. I could give you a ring at work . . .

12 EILEEN. You don't know where I work.

13 STAN. Dixon's cream crackers, back of the Albert Monument . . .

14 EILEEN. I didn't tell you that . . .

15 STAN. I don't work at the Labour Exchange for nothing . . .

16 EILEEN. We're not allowed to have personal calls.

17 STAN. Get weaving with the old classified, you can't go wrong . . .

18 EILEEN. I'll get the sack . . .

19 STAN. What did you say your second name was, you know, just for old time's sake?

20 EILEEN. Your collar's undone again.

21 STAN. It's stopping undone.

22 EILEEN. Shut the gate quietly when you go.

23 STAN. Right at the traffic lights was it?

24 EILEEN. Yes. Good night then, Stan.

25 STAN. Good night, Eileen. See you sometime, perhaps. [*He has given up.*]

1 EILEEN. Perhaps.

   Pause.

   Stan.

2 STAN [*from a distance*]. Yes.

3 EILEEN. I'm on the switchboard between ten and half-past eleven.

4 STAN. Sorry. I'm not allowed to make personal calls, like Hell.

   Fade out.

Fade in fog-horns and miscellaneous night noises, slightly unreal. STAN *walking home in the small hours.*

5 STAN. By heck, there's something to be said for the old girl-next-door. Three miles? More like three hundred. Be glad when I get to 'The Grapes'. Don't go much for this playing away. Hey! There's someone following me, I can hear him. I'll go up a gear, just to check, there, yes, he's hurrying up as well. It'll be one of these Teds, there's hundreds of them on these estates. He'll be after knocking my hat off. Go on then, try it! Just you try it! I'll fill him in, if he does. I think I'll run a bit. He's running as well ... you silly idiot! It's your echo. Blimey, gives you a turn, owt like that. I can see The Grapes, thank heaven for that, I must be on the right road ... three miles ... mind you, she's all right, Eileen, she's a nice lass. Blue eyes. Brown? Have to check. Did all right then, Jack?

6 JACK. You're on a good number, mate.

7 STAN. That's what I thought.

8 JACK. Boy-friend in the R.A.F., can't go wrong.

9 STAN. It's a problem that.

10 JACK. It's perfect, really.

11 STAN. No it isn't, it's a blooming nuisance.

1 JACK. You knock around with her for a few weeks, have a bit of fun, then old Bleriot comes back from the wars, you disappear. Marvellous.

2 STAN [*outraged*]. What you talking about?

3 JACK. It's a question of having a good time, without getting landed with any responsibilities. I mean, the kid's lonely, you're doing her a favour, it's only natural . . .

4 STAN. Supposing I don't want to give her back to this intrepid birdman?

5 JACK. Stan.

6 STAN. Yes, Jack?

7 JACK. I don't quite know how to put this. You wouldn't be . . . purely as a long-term policy, you understand . . . contemplating marriage to this bird.

8 STAN. Maybe, early yet like.

9 JACK. Look Stan, I don't want you to get the wrong idea. I mean, it's all right, slippers in the hearth, but there's a big price to pay. Gardens to dig, wallpapering to be done, and hundreds, believe me, Stan, hundreds upon hundreds of shelves to be put up. Mind you, sometimes there's shelves to be taken down cause they're in the wrong place. Carpets to be laid, payments to keep up, just give us a hand with the washing-up, love . . .

10 STAN. Brown, definitely brown.

11 JACK. You'll never see the inside of The Grapes again. Goodbye for ever, double-top, farewell pink and black for game.

12 STAN. No, brown, not pink, Jack. Who ever heard of pink eyes.

13 JACK. I could have wept when she kept straightening your tie, getting you tidied up . . . I could just see it, hurry up, love, you'll be late for work, have you got your sandwiches . . . ? Cheese, don't worry, it'll be cheese, every day. And you'll have to keep the same job, all the time . . .

1   STAN. Well, five in a year's a bit much, makes a mess of your stamp card.

2   JACK. So help me, Stan, I give in. I should have made you go to the wrestling. I don't think much to the Masked Vampire, but he wouldn't have put any daft ideas in your head.

3   STAN [*conclusively*]. Good night, Jack.

4   JACK. Looks like I've been wasting my time. Breaks your heart, doesn't it? All right. See you in church.

Fade out.

The Hargreaves' living room. STAN *opens the door.*

5   STAN. Blimey, are you still up? Don't you know what time it is?

6   MRS. HARGREAVES. Oh, hello, Stan, yes, I know what time it is. Your Auntie Dora called and could I heck as get rid of her. Talk, talk, talk . . .

7   STAN. Glad I wasn't in.

8   MRS. HARGREAVES. She was after her supper, like, but I wasn't having that. I thought no, milady, I can wait longer than you. Would you like a cup of tea, Stan?

9   STAN. Ta.

10   MRS. HARGREAVES. I haven't forgotten that business about the china cabinet . . .

11   STAN. You should have got Dad to talk to her.

12   MRS. HARGREAVES. What? The sleeping beauty . . . he's been well away all night.

13   STAN. I'll wake him up. Come on, wakey, wakey! Not a murmur.

14   MRS. HARGREAVES. I wouldn't care, but his head keeps slipping off the chair back and he half wakes up, and puts it back, you know, drives me crackers when he does that . . .

1   STAN. Come on, wake up, Dad, time for bed . . . [*Shouting suddenly.*] Penalty, ref!

2   MR. HARGREAVES [*startled*]. What? What is it?

3   MRS. HARGREAVES. Your tea's on table, Stan, I put sugar in...

4   MR. HARGREAVES. What time is it?

5   STAN. Nearly one o'clock.

6   MR. HARGREAVES. Have you just come in? Where've you been till now?

7   STAN. Out.

8   MRS. HARGREAVES. Aye, where did you go? Did you have a good time?

9   MR. HARGREAVES. He'll have been up to something, I bet . .

10   STAN. Just been out, that's all . . .

11   MR. HARGREAVES. Aye, letting somebody's tyres down I shouldn't wonder . . .

12   STAN. Don't be daft, course I haven't . . .

13   MR. HARGREAVES. Fellow at the match was telling me, busting wireless aerials off cars, that's the latest game.

14   STAN. I'm not a flipping delinquent . . .

15   MR. HARGREAVES. They're all alike when they get dressed up, goes to their heads, too much money, that's the trouble . . .

16   MRS. HARGREAVES. Oh, shuttup, Dad, you're always at him. He hasn't even told us where he's been yet . . .

17   STAN. What?

18   MRS. HARGREAVES. You haven't told us where you've been.

19   STAN. Oh, no. [*Vague.*] What's Auntie Dora have to say then?

20   MRS. HARGREAVES. She hardly stopped. I don't mind a bit of gossip but she goes too far, you know, it's not right. She's nasty with it.

21   MR. HARGREAVES. She's just nasty.

22   MRS. HARGREAVES. Apparently your cousin Wilfred's been seen in Harrogate . . .

1 STAN. Oh aye.

2 MRS. HARGREAVES. Course, Florrie's all upset again, just as she was getting over it as well ... don't go mentioning it, either of you, will you?

3 STAN. No we won't say owt, will we, Dad?

MR. HARGREAVES *grunts.*

4 MRS. HARGREAVES. And she said something else, as well, what was it again ... oh, aye, your old friend Jack.

5 STAN. Jack?

6 MRS. HARGREAVES. Jack. You didn't tell me, Stanley, that Jack ... well ... had to get married in a hurry. You know what I mean.

7 STAN. No, I didn't tell you.

8 MRS. HARGREAVES. Why not?

9 STAN. I ... well, I didn't think it was very important.

10 MRS. HARGREAVES. You didn't think it was very important!

11 STAN. Well, it was important ... for Jack. But I thought it was best not to crack on to too many people.

12 MRS. HARGREAVES. Well I was very surprised, I always thought he seemed such a nice young lad ...

13 MR. HARGREAVES. It's just what I've always said ...

14 MRS. HARGREAVES. He was always very polite when he used to come here.

15 MR. HARGREAVES. They're all alike these days, you can't be too sure with any of them ...

16 STAN. Well, it just happened ... he did the right thing, he married her.

17 MR. HARGREAVES. Well, I'd have them locked up, the lot of them.

18 STAN. You'd have everybody locked up, except flaming footballers ...

19 MR. HARGREAVES. He talked too smooth, you got to watch them when they talk smooth ... overmuch gas, like.

1 STAN. Yes, I know what you mean.

2 MR. HARGREAVES. What?

3 STAN. Don't know really, sort of got into the habit of going around with him. Didn't have that much in common really.

4 MR. HARGREAVES. I hope not.

5 MRS. HARGREAVES. Anyway, he's settled down now.

6 MR. HARGREAVES. Damn sight safer for everybody with him out the way.

Pause.

7 STAN. Bit of a big-head, really.

8 MR. HARGREAVES. About time you realized.

9 STAN. Yes, you're right there. You're definitely right there [*Yawns.*] Just about bedtime.

10 MRS. HARGREAVES. What you straightening your tie for, if you're off to bed?

11 STAN [*casual*]. Just like to be tidy, you know . . .

12 MR. HARGREAVES. You what?

13 STAN. Can't go around looking like a tramp, you know.

14 MR. HARGREAVES. Well, take your flipping hat off in the house·

15 STAN. Sorry.

16 MR. HARGREAVES. In a flaming trance again. Always dreaming, look at him, combing his hair.

17 MRS. HARGREAVES. It's nice to see him taking a bit of pride in his appearance.

18 MR. HARGREAVES. No chance of him getting into trouble, no lass'd look at him.

19 STAN. No, I won't get into trouble, Dad. It'll be bells and toast-racks and Co-op catering when I go . . .

20 MRS. HARGREAVES. Stanley . . .

21 MR. HARGREAVES. What you talking about now?

22 STAN. Oh well, time for byesie-byes. Night, all.

The door closes behind him.

1 MR. HARGREAVES. He's been drinking.

2 MRS. HARGREAVES. That's what you think.

3 MR. HARGREAVES. You what?

4 MRS. HARGREAVES. Oh, look, he hasn't drunk his tea again . .

5 MR. HARGREAVES. Why, he doesn't listen half the time, I'm fed up of telling him . . .

6 MRS. HARGREAVES. I'll just clear away, I don't like pots lying around on the table . . .

7 MR. HARGREAVES. He wants a good shaking up . . .

STAN *opens the door and comes back into the room.*

8 STAN. Hey, Dad . . .

9 MR. HARGREAVES. You didn't drink your tea . . .

10 STAN. Changed my mind, didn't want it . . .

11 MR. HARGREAVES. The times I've told you about . . .

12 STAN. Don't worry. We'll fix it when United's playing away.

13 MR. HARGREAVES. You what?

14 STAN. We'll check the fixtures, don't worry . . .

Fade out.

The Dock Brief

by John Mortimer

Cast:

MORGENHALL

FOWLE

✳ ✳ ✳
The Dock Brief

Fade in the echoing sound of a cell door being unlocked.

MORGENHALL [*a fussy, elderly and educated voice*]. Is this where . . . you keep Mr. Fowle? Good, excellent. Then leave us alone like a kind fellow. And no interruptions. Would you mind closing the door? These old places are so draughty.

The door closes with a hollow thud, bolts shoot back.

Mr. Fowle . . . Where are you, Mr. Fowle? I pray he hasn't escaped by any chance. Oh, up there. Good heavens, man, come down. Come down, Mr. Fowle.

Sounds of a scuffle as a chair or stool is overturned. The two men gasp as they sway together. Then the stool is set up again.

I haven't hurt you?

FOWLE, *negative sounding noise.*

I was suddenly anxious. A man in your unfortunate position. Desperate measures. And I couldn't bear to lose you. . . . No, don't stand up. It's difficult for you without braces, or a belt, I can see. And no tie, no shoe-laces. I'm so glad they're looking after you. You must forgive me if I frightened you just a little, Mr. Fowle. It was when I saw you up by that window . . .

FOWLE [*a hoarse and sad voice*]. Epping Forest.

3 MORGENHALL. What did you say?

4 FOWLE. I think you can see Epping Forest.

5 MORGENHALL. No doubt you can. But why, my dear chap, should you want to?

6 FOWLE. It's the home stretch.

7 MORGENHALL. Very well.

1   FOWLE. I thought I could get a glimpse of the green. Between the chimney and that shed. . . .

    FOWLE *starts to climb up again. A brief renewed struggle.*

2   MORGENHALL. No, get down. It's not wise to be up there, forever trying to look out. There's a draughty, sneeping wind. Treacherous.

3   FOWLE. Treacherous?

4   MORGENHALL. I'm afraid so. You never know what a mean, sneeping wind can do. Catch you by the throat, start a sneeze, then a dry tickle on the chest. I don't want anything to catch you like that before. . . .

5   FOWLE. Before what?

6   MORGENHALL. You're much better sitting quietly down there in the warm. Just sit quietly and I'll introduce myself.

7   FOWLE. I'm tired.

8   MORGENHALL. I'm Wilfred Morgenhall.

9   FOWLE. Wilfred?

10   MORGENHALL. Morgenhall. The barrister.

11   FOWLE. The barrister?

12   MORGENHALL. Perfectly so. . . .

13   FOWLE. I'm sorry.

14   MORGENHALL. Why?

15   FOWLE. A barrister, That's very bad.

16   MORGENHALL. I don't know. Why's it so bad?

17   FOWLE. When a gentleman of your stamp goes wrong. A long fall.

18   MORGENHALL. What can you mean?

19   FOWLE. Different for an individual like me. I only kept a small seed shop.

20   MORGENHALL. Seed shop? My poor fellow. We mustn't let this unfortunate little case confuse us. We're going to remain very calm, very lucid. We're going to come to important decisions. Now, do me a favour, Mr. Fowle, no more seed shops.

1   FOWLE. Birdseed, of course. Individuals down our way kept
    birds mostly. Canaries and budgies. The budgies talked.
    Lot of lonely people down our way. They kept them
    for the talk.

2   MORGENHALL. I know the law.

3   FOWLE. It's trapped you.

4   MORGENHALL. I'm here to help you.

5   FOWLE. We'll help each other.

    Pause.

6   MORGENHALL [*laughs uncontrollably*]. I see. Mr. Fowle. I see
    where you've been bewildered. You think I'm in
    trouble as well. Then I've got news for you at last. I'm
    free. Oh yes. I can leave here when I like.

7   FOWLE. You can?

8   MORGENHALL. The police are my friends.

9   FOWLE. They are?

10 MORGENHALL. And I've never felt better in my life. There
    now. That's relieved you, hasn't it? I'm not in any
    trouble.

11 FOWLE. Family all well.

12 MORGENHALL. I never married.

13 FOWLE. Rent paid up?

14 MORGENHALL. A week or two owing perhaps. Temporary
    lull in business. This case will end all that.

15 FOWLE. Which case?

16 MORGENHALL. Your case.

17 FOWLE. My . . . ?

18 MORGENHALL. Case.

19 FOWLE. Oh that—it's not important.

20 MORGENHALL. Not?

21 FOWLE. I don't care about it to any large extent. Not as at
    present advised.

1 MORGENHALL. Mr. Fowle. How could you say that?

2 FOWLE. The flavour's gone out of it.

3 MORGENHALL. But we're only at the beginning.

4 FOWLE. I can't believe it's me concerned.

5 MORGENHALL. But it is you, Mr. Fowle. You mustn't let yourself forget that. You see, that's why you're here....

6 FOWLE. I can't seem to bother with it.

7 MORGENHALL. Can you be so busy ?

8 FOWLE. Slopping in, slopping out. Peering at the old forest. It fills in the day.

9 MORGENHALL. You seem, if I may say so, to have adopted an unpleasantly selfish attitude.

10 FOWLE. Selfish?

11 MORGENHALL. Dog in the manger.

12 FOWLE. In the?

13 MORGENHALL. Unenthusiastic.

14 FOWLE. You're speaking quite frankly, I well appreciate. . . .

15 MORGENHALL. I'm sorry, Fowle. You made me say it. There's so much of this about nowadays. There's so much ready made entertainment. Free billiards. National Health. Television. There's not the spirit abroad there used to be.

16 FOWLE. You feel that?

17 MORGENHALL. Whatever I've done I've always been mustard keen on my work. I've never lost the vision, Fowle. In all my disappointments I've never lost the love of the job.

18 FOWLE. The position in life you've obtained to.

19 MORGENHALL. Years of study I had to put in. It didn't just drop in my lap.

20 FOWLE. I've never studied. . . .

21 MORGENHALL. Year after year, Fowle, my window at college was alight until two a.m. There I sat among my books. I fed mainly on herrings. . . .

1 FOWLE. Lean years?

2 MORGENHALL. And black tea. No subsidised biscuits then, Fowle, no County Council tobacco, just work. . . .

3 FOWLE. Book work, almost entirely? I'm only assuming that, of course.

4 MORGENHALL. Want to hear some Latin?

5 FOWLE. Only if you have time.

6 MORGENHALL. *Actus non sit reus nisi mens sit rea. Filius nullius. In flagrante delicto.* Understand it?

7 FOWLE. I'm no scholar.

8 MORGENHALL. You most certainly are not. But I had to be, we all had to be in my day. Then we'd sit for all the examinations, Mods, Smalls, Greats, Tripos, Little Goes, week after week, rowing men fainting, Indian students vomiting with fear, and no creeping out for a peep at the book under the pretext of a pump ship or getting a glance at the other fellow's celluloid cuff. . .

9 FOWLE. That would be unheard of?

10 MORGENHALL. Then weeks, months of waiting. Nerve racking. Go up to the Lake District. Pace the mountains, play draughts, forget to huff. Then comes the fatal postcard.

11 FOWLE. What's it say?

12 MORGENHALL. Satisfied the examiners.

13 FOWLE. At last!

14 MORGENHALL. Don't rejoice so soon. True enough I felt I'd turned a corner, got a fur hood, bumped on the head with a Bible. Bachelor of Law sounded sweet in my ears. I thought of celebrating, a few kindred spirits round for a light ale. Told the only lady in my life that in five year's time perhaps. . . .

15 FOWLE. You'd arrived.

16 MORGENHALL. That's what I thought when they painted my name up on the London chambers. I sat down to fill in the time until they sent my first brief in a real case.

I sat down to do the crossword puzzle while I waited. Five years later, Fowle, what was I doing. . . .

2   FOWLE. A little charge of High Treason?

3   MORGENHALL. I was still doing the crossword puzzle.

4   FOWLE. But better at it?

5   MORGENHALL. Not much. Not very much. As the years pass there come to be clues you no longer understand.

6   FOWLE. So all that training?

7   MORGENHALL. Wasted. The talents rust.

8   FOWLE. And the lady?

9   MORGENHALL. Drove an ambulance in the 1914. A stray piece of shrapnel took her. I don't care to talk of it.

10 FOWLE. Tragic.

11 MORGENHALL. What was?

12 FOWLE. Tragic my wife was never called up.

13 MORGENHALL. You mustn't talk like that, Fowle, your poor wife.

14 FOWLE. Don't let's carry on about me.

15 MORGENHALL. But we must carry on about you. That's what I'm here for.

16 FOWLE. You're here to?

17 MORGENHALL. Defend you.

18 FOWLE. Can't be done.

19 MORGENHALL. Why ever not?

20 FOWLE. I know who killed her.

21 MORGENHALL. Who?

22 FOWLE. Me.

   Pause.

23 MORGENHALL [*considerable thought before he says*]. Mr. Fowle, I have all the respect in the world for your opinions, but we must face this. You're a man of very little education. . . .

24 FOWLE. That's true.

1 MORGENHALL. One has only to glance at you. At those curious lobes to your ears. At the line of your hair. At the strange way your eyebrows connect in the middle, to see that you're a person of very limited intelligence.

2 FOWLE. Agreed, quite frankly.

3 MORGENHALL. You think you killed your wife.

4 FOWLE. Seems so to me.

5 MORGENHALL. Mr. Fowle. Look at yourself objectively. On questions of birdseed I have no doubt you may be infallible—but on a vital point like this might you not be mistaken. . . . Don't answer. . . .

6 FOWLE. Why not, sir?

7 MORGENHALL. Before you drop the bomb of a reply, consider who will be wounded. Are the innocent to suffer?

8 FOWLE. I only want to be honest.

9 MORGENHALL. But you're a criminal, Mr. Fowle. You've broken through the narrow fabric of honesty. You are free to be kind, human, to do good.

10 FOWLE. But what I did to her. . . .

11 MORGENHALL. She's passed, you know, out of your life. You've set up new relationships. You've picked out me.

12 FOWLE. Picked out?

13 MORGENHALL. Selected.

14 FOWLE. But I didn't know. . . .

15 MORGENHALL. No, Mr. Fowle. That's the whole beauty of it. You didn't know me. You came to see me under a system of chance inverted, like football pools, to even out the harsh inequality of a world where you have to deserve success. You, Mr. Fowle, are my first Dock Brief.

16 FOWLE. Your Dock?

17 MORGENHALL. Brief.

18 FOWLE. You couldn't explain?

1 MORGENHALL. Of course. Prisoners with no money and no friends exist. Luckily, you're one of them. They're entitled to choose any barrister sitting in Court to defend them. The barrister, however old, gets a brief, and is remunerated on a modest scale. Busy lawyers, wealthy lawyers, men with other interests creep out of Court bent double when the Dock Brief is chosen. We regulars who are not busy sit on. I've been a regular for years. It's not etiquette, you see, even if you want the work, to wave at the prisoner, or whistle, or try to catch his eye by hoisting any sort of little flag.

2 FOWLE. Didn't know.

3 MORGENHALL. But you can choose the most advantageous seat. The seat any criminal would naturally point at. It's the seat under the window and for ten years my old friend Tuppy Morgan, bagged it each day at ten. He sat there reading Horace, and writing to his innumerable aunts, and almost once a year a criminal pointed him out. Oh, Mr. Fowle, Tuppy was a limpet on that seat. But this morning, something, possibly a cold, perhaps death, kept him indoors. So I had his place. And you spotted me, no doubt.

4 FOWLE. Spotted you?

5 MORGENHALL. My glasses polished. My profile drawn and learned in front of the great window.

6 FOWLE. I never noticed.

7 MORGENHALL. But when they asked you to choose a lawyer?

8 FOWLE. I shut my eyes and pointed—I've picked horses that way, and football teams. Never did me any good, though, by any stretch of the imagination.

9 MORGENHALL. So even you, Mr. Fowle, didn't choose me?

10 FOWLE. Not altogether.

11 MORGENHALL. The law's a haphazard business.

12 FOWLE. It does seem chancy.

1   MORGENHALL. Years of training, and then to be picked out like a football pool.

2   FOWLE. Don't take it badly, sir.

3   MORGENHALL. Of course, you've been fortunate.

4   FOWLE. So unusual. I was never one to draw the free bird at Christmas, or guess the weight of the cake. Now I'm sorry I told you.

5   MORGENHALL. Never mind. You hurt me temporarily, Fowle, I must confess. It might have been kinder to have kept me in ignorance. But now it's done. Let's get down to business. And, Fowle—

6   FOWLE. Yes, sir.

7   MORGENHALL. Remember you're dealing with fellow man. A man no longer young. Remember the hopes I've pinned on you and try. . . .

8   FOWLE. Try?

9   MORGENHALL. Try to spare me more pain.

10   FOWLE. I will, sir. Of course I will.

11   MORGENHALL. Now. Let's get our minds in order.

12   FOWLE. Sort things out.

13   MORGENHALL. Exactly. Now, this wife of yours.

14   FOWLE. Doris?

15   MORGENHALL. Doris. A bitter, unsympathetic woman?

16   FOWLE. She was always cheerful. She loved jokes.

17   MORGENHALL. Oh, Fowle. Do be careful.

18   FOWLE. I will, sir. But if you'd known Doris. . . . She laughed harder than she worked. 'Thank God,' she'd say, 'for my old English sense of fun.'

19   MORGENHALL. What sort of jokes, Fowle, did this Doris appreciate?

20   FOWLE. All sorts. Pictures in the paper. Jokes on the wireless set. Laughs out of crackers, she'd keep them from Christmas to Christmas and trot them out in August.

21   MORGENHALL. You couldn't share it?

1   FOWLE. Not to that extent. I often missed the funny point.

2   MORGENHALL. Then you'd quarrel?

3   FOWLE. 'Don't look so miserable, it may never happen.' She said that every night when I came home. 'Where'd you get that miserable expression from?'

4   MORGENHALL. I can see it now. There is a kind of Sunday evening appearance to you.

5   FOWLE. I was quite happy. But it was always 'Cat got your tongue?' 'Where's the funeral?' 'Play us a tune on that old fiddle face of yours. Lucky there's one of us here that can see the funny side.' Then we had to have our tea with the wireless on, so that she'd pick up the phrases.

6   MORGENHALL. You're not a wireless lover?

7   FOWLE. I couldn't always laugh. And she'd be doubled up across the table, gasping as if her lungs were full of water. 'Laugh,' she'd call, 'Laugh, damn you. What've you got to be so miserable about?' Then she'd go under, bubbling like a drowning woman.

8   MORGENHALL. Made meals difficult?

9   FOWLE. Indigestible. I would have laughed, but the jokes never tickled me.

10   MORGENHALL. They tickled her?

11   FOWLE. Anything did. Anything a little comic. Our names were misfortunate.

12   MORGENHALL. Your names?

13   FOWLE. Fowle. Going down the aisle she said: 'Now we're cock and hen, aren't we, old bird?' Coming away, it was 'Now I'm Mrs. Fowle, you'll have to play fair with me.' She laughed so hard we couldn't get her straightened for the photograph.

14   MORGENHALL. Fond of puns, I gather you're trying to say.

15   FOWLE. Of any sort of joke. I had a little aviary at the bottom of my garden. As she got funnier so I spent more time with my birds. Budgerigars are small parrots. Circles round their eyes give them a sad, tired look.

1 MORGENHALL. You found them sympathetic?

2 FOWLE. Restful. Until one of them spoke out at me.

3 MORGENHALL. Spoke—what words?

4 FOWLE. 'Don't look so miserable, it may never happen.'

5 MORGENHALL. The bird said that?

6 FOWLE. She taught it during the day when I was out at work. It didn't mean to irritate.

7 MORGENHALL. It was wrong of her of course. To lead on your bird like that.

8 FOWLE. But it wasn't him that brought me to it. It was Bateson, the lodger.

9 MORGENHALL. Another man?

10 FOWLE. At long last.

11 MORGENHALL. I can see it now. A crime of passion. An unfaithful wife. *In flagrante.* . . . Of course, you don't know what that means. We'll reduce it to manslaughter right away. A wronged husband and there's never a dry eye in the jury-box. You came in and caught them.

12 FOWLE. Always laughing together.

13 MORGENHALL. Maddening.

14 FOWLE. He knew more jokes than she did.

15 MORGENHALL. Stealing her before your eyes?

16 FOWLE. That's what I thought. He was a big man. Ex-police. Said he'd been the scream of the station. I picked him for her specially. In the chitty I put up in the local sweet shop, I wrote. 'Humerous type of lodger wanted.'

17 MORGENHALL. But wasn't that a risk?

18 FOWLE. Slight, perhaps. But it went all right. Two days after he came he poised a bag of flour to fall on her in the kitchen. Then she sewed up the legs of his pyjamas. They had to hold on to each other so as not to fall over laughing. 'Look at old misery standing there,' she said. 'He can never see anything subtle.'

19 MORGENHALL. Galling for you. Terribly galling.

1 FOWLE. I thought all was well. I spent more time with the birds. I'd come home late and always be careful to scrunch the gravel at the front door. I went to bed early and left them with the Light Programme. On Sunday mornings I fed the budgies and suggested he took her tea in bed. 'Laughter,' she read out from her horoscope, 'leads to love, even for those born under the sign of the virgin.'

2 MORGENHALL. You trusted them. They deceived you.

3 FOWLE. They deceived me all right. And I trusted them. Especially after I'd seen her on his knee and them both looking at the cartoons from one wrapping of chips.

4 MORGENHALL. Mr. Fowle. I'm not quite getting the drift of your evidence. My hope is—your thought may not prove a shade too involved for our literal-minded judge. Old Tommy Banter was a Rugger blue in '98. He never rose to chess and his draughts had a brutal, unintelligent quality.

5 FOWLE. When he'd first put his knee under her I thought he'd do the decent thing. I thought I'd have peace in my little house at last . . . The wireless set dead silent . . . The end of all that happy laughter . . . No sound but the twitter from the end of the garden and the squeak of my own foot on the linoleum.

6 MORGENHALL. You wanted. . . .

7 FOWLE. I heard them whispering together and my hopes raised high. Then I came back and he was gone.

8 MORGENHALL. She'd. . . .

9 FOWLE. Turned him out. Because he was getting over-familiar. 'I couldn't have that.' she said. 'I may like my laugh, but I'm still respectable. No thank you, there's safety in marriage. So I'm stuck with you, fiddle face. Let's play a tune on it, shall we?' She'd sent him away, my last hope.

10 MORGENHALL. So you. . . .

11 FOWLE. I realize I did wrong.

1 MORGENHALL. You could have left.

2 FOWLE. Who'd have fed the birds? That thought was uppermost.

3 MORGENHALL. So it's not a crime of passion?

4 FOWLE. Not if you put it like that.

5 MORGENHALL. Mr. Fowle. I've worked and waited for you. Now, you're the only case I've got, and the most difficult.

6 FOWLE. I'm sorry.

7 MORGENHALL. A man like me could crack his head against a case like you and still be far from a solution. Can't you see how twelve honest hearts will snap like steel when they learn you ended up your wife because she *wouldn't* leave you?

8 FOWLE. If she had left, there wouldn't have been the need.

9 MORGENHALL. There's no doubt about it. As I look at you now, I see you're an unsympathetic figure.

10 FOWLE. There it is.

11 MORGENHALL. It'll need a brilliant stroke to save you. An unexpected move—something pulled out of a hat—I've got it. Something really exciting. The surprise witness.

12 FOWLE. Witness?

13 MORGENHALL. Picture the scene, Mr. Fowle. The Court room silent. The jury about to sink you. The prosecution flushed with victory. And then I rise, my voice a hoarse whisper, exhausted by that long trial. 'My Lord. If your Lordship pleases.'

14 FOWLE. What are you saying?

15 MORGENHALL. Do you expect me to do this off the cuff. Fowle, with no sort of rehearsal?

16 FOWLE. No. . . .

17 MORGENHALL. Take the stool and co-operate, man. Now, that towel over your head, please, to stimulate the dirty grey wig—already you appear anonymous and vaguely alarming. Now my dear Fowle, forget your

personality. You're Sir Tommy Banter, living with a widowed sister in a draughty great morgue on Wimbledon Common. Digestion, bad. Politics, an independent moral conservative. Favourite author, doesn't read. Diversions, snooker in the basement of the morgue peeping at the lovers on the Common, and money being given away on the television. In love with capital punishment, corporal punishment, and a younger brother who is accomplished at embroidery. A small, alarmed man, frightened of the great dog he lives with to give him the air of a country squire. Served with distinction in the Great War at sentencing soldiers to long terms of imprisonment. A man without friends, unexpectedly adored by a great-niece, three years old.

2   FOWLE. I am?

3   MORGENHALL. Him.

4   FOWLE. It feels strange.

5   MORGENHALL. Now, my Lord. I ask your Lordship's leave to call the surprise witness.

6   FOWLE. Certainly.

7   MORGENHALL. What?

8   FOWLE. Certainly.

9   MORGENHALL. For Heaven's sake, Fowle, this is like practising bull-fights with a kitten. Here's an irregular application by the defence, something that might twist the trial in the prisoner's favour and prevent you catching the connection at Charing Cross. Your breakfast's like a leadweight on your chest, your sister, plunging at Spot last night, ripped the cloth. The dog bit your ankle on the way downstairs. No, blind yourself with rage and terrible justice.

10 FOWLE. No. You can't call the surprise witness.

11 MORGENHALL. That's better. Oh, my Lord. If your Lordship would listen to me.

1 FOWLE. Certainly not. You've had your chance. Let's get on with it.

2 MORGENHALL. My Lord. Justice must not only be done, but must clearly be seen to be done. No one knows, as yet, what my surprise witness will say. Perhaps he'll say the prisoner is guilty in his black heart as your Lordship thinks. But perhaps, gentlemen of the jury, we have trapped an innocent. If so, shall we deny him the one door through which he might walk to freedom? The public outcry would never die down.

3 FOWLE. Hear, hear!

4 MORGENHALL. What's that?

5 FOWLE. The public outcry.

6 MORGENHALL. Excellent. Now, towel back on. You're the judge.

7 FOWLE [*as the* JUDGE]. Silence! I'll have all those noisy people put out. Very well. Call the witness. But keep it short.

8 MORGENHALL. Wonderful. Very good. Now. Deathly silence as the witness walks through the breathless crowds. Let's see the surprise witness. Take the towel off. You can't stand up, of course.

9 FOWLE. I swear to tell the truth . . .

10 MORGENHALL. You've got a real feeling for the Law. A pity you came to it so late in life.

11 FOWLE. The whole truth.

12 MORGENHALL. Now, what's your name?

13 FOWLE [*absent minded*]. Herbert Fowle.

14 MORGENHALL. No, no. You're the witness.

15 FOWLE. Martin Jones.

16 MORGENHALL. Excellent, Now, you know Herbert Fowle?

17 FOWLE. All my life.

18 MORGENHALL. Always found him respectable?

19 FOWLE. Very quiet spoken man, and clean living.

1 MORGENHALL. Where was he when the crime took place?

2 FOWLE. He was. . . .

3 MORGENHALL. Just a moment. My Lord, will you sharpen a
   pencil and note this down?

4 FOWLE. You'd dare to say that? To him?

5 MORGENHALL. Fearlessness, Mr. Fowle. The first essential in
   an advocate. Is your Lordship's pencil poised?

6 FOWLE [*as* JUDGE]. Yes, yes. Get on with it.

7 MORGENHALL. Where was he?

8 FOWLE [*as* WITNESS]. In my house.

9 MORGENHALL. All the evening?

10 FOWLE. Playing whist. I went to collect him and we left Mrs.
   Fowle well and happy. I returned with him and she'd
   been removed to the Country and General.

11 MORGENHALL. Panic stirs the prosecution benches. The
   prosecutor tries a few fumbling questions. But you
   stand your ground, don't you?

12 FOWLE. Certainly.

13 MORGENHALL. My Lord. I demand the prisoner be released.

14 FOWLE [*as* JUDGE]. Certainly. Can't think what all the fuss has
   been about. Release the prisoner, and reduce all the
   police officers in Court to the rank of P.C.

   Pause.

15 MORGENHALL. Fowle.

16 FOWLE. Yes, sir.

17 MORGENHALL. Aren't you going to thank me?

18 FOWLE. I don't know what I can say.

19 MORGENHALL. Words don't come easily to you, do they?

20 FOWLE. Very hard.

21 MORGENHALL. You could just stand and stammer in a touch-
   ing way and offer me that old gold watch of your
   father's.

1   FOWLE. But. . . .

2   MORGENHALL. Fowle, you're a good simple chap, but there's no need to interrupt my thinking.

3   FOWLE. I was only reminding you. . . .

4   MORGENHALL. Well, what?

5   FOWLE. We have no Jones.

6   MORGENHALL. Carried off in a cold spell? Then we can get his statement in under the Evidence Act.

7   FOWLE. He never lived. We made it up.

Pause.

8   MORGENHALL. Fowle.

9   FOWLE. Yes, sir.

10 MORGENHALL. It's a remarkable thing, but with no legal training, I think you've put your finger on a fatal weakness in our defence.

11 FOWLE. I was afraid it might be so.

12 MORGENHALL. It is so.

13 FOWLE. Then we'd better just give in.

14 MORGENHALL. Give in? We do not give in. When my life depends on this case.

15 FOWLE. I forgot. Then, we must try.

16 MORGENHALL. Yes. Brain! Brain! Go to work. It'll come to me, you know, in an illuminating flash. Hard relentless brain work. This is the way I go at the crosswords and I never give up. I have it Bateson!

17 FOWLE. The lodger?

18 MORGENHALL. Bateson, the lodger. I never liked him. Under a ruthless cross-examination, you know, he might confess that it was he. Do you see a flash?

19 FOWLE. You look much happier.

20 MORGENHALL. I am much happier. And when I begin my ruthless cross-examination . . .

21 FOWLE. Would you care to try it?

1 MORGENHALL. Mr. FOWLE. You and I are learning to muck in splendidly together over this. Mr. Bateson.

2 FOWLE [*as* BATESON]. Yes. Sir?

3 MORGENHALL. Perhaps, when you address the Court you'd be good enough to take your hands out of your pockets. Not you Mr. Fowle, of course. You became on very friendly terms with the prisoner's wife?

4 FOWLE. We had one or two good old laughs together.

5 MORGENHALL. Was the association entirely innocent?

6 FOWLE. Innocent laughs. Jokes without offence. The cracker or Christmas card variety. No jokes that would have shamed a postcard.

7 MORGENHALL. And to tell those innocent jokes, did you have to sit very close to Mrs. Fowle?

8 FOWLE. How do you mean?

9 MORGENHALL. Did you have to sit beneath her?

10 FOWLE. I don't understand.

11 MORGENHALL. Did she perch upon your knee?

12 FOWLE [*horrified intake of breath*].

13 MORGENHALL. What was that?

14 FOWLE. Shocked breathing from the jury, sir.

15 MORGENHALL. Having its effect, eh? Now, Mr. Bateson. Will you kindly answer my question.

16 FOWLE. You're trying to trap me.

17 MORGENHALL. Not trying, Bateson, succeeding.

18 FOWLE. Well, she may have rested on my knee. Once or twice.

19 MORGENHALL. And you loved her, guiltily?

20 FOWLE. I may have done.

21 MORGENHALL. And planned to take her away with you?

22 FOWLE. I did ask her.

23 MORGENHALL. And when she refused . . .

24 FOWLE [*as* JUDGE]. Just a moment. Where's all this leading?

1 MORGENHALL. Your Lordship asks me! My Lord, it is our case that it was this man, Bateson, enraged by the refusal of the prisoner's wife to follow him, who struck.... You see where we've got to?

2 FOWLE. I do.

3 MORGENHALL. Masterly. I think you'll have to agree with me?

4 FOWLE. Of course.

5 MORGENHALL. No flaws in this one?

6 FOWLE. Not really a flaw, sir. Perhaps a little hitch.

7 MORGENHALL. A hitch. Go on. Break it down.

8 FOWLE. No, sir, really. Not after you've been so kind.

9 MORGENHALL. Never mind. All my life I've stood against the winds of criticism and neglect. My gown may be a little tattered, my cuffs frayed, There may be a hole in my sock for the draughts to get at me. Quite often, on my way to Court, I notice that my left shoe lets in water. I am used to hardship. Speak on, Mr. Fowle.

10 FOWLE. Soon as he left my house, Bateson was stopped by an officer. He'd lifted an alarm clock off me, and the remains of a bottle of port. They booked him straight away.

11 MORGENHALL. You mean, there wasn't time?

12 FOWLE. Hardly. Two hours later the next door observed Mrs. Fowle at the washing. Then I came home.

13 MORGENHALL. Fowle. Do you want to help me?

14 FOWLE. Of course. Haven't I shown it?

15 MORGENHALL. But you will go on putting all these difficulties in my way.

16 FOWLE. I knew you'd be upset.

17 MORGENHALL. Not really. After all, I'm a grown-up, even an old man. At my age one expects little gratitude. There's a cat I feed each day at my lodgings, a waitress in the lunch room here who always gets that sixpence under my plate. In ten, twenty years' time, will they remember me? Oh, I'm not bitter. But a little help, just a very little encouragement. . . .

1 FOWLE. But you'll win the case. A brilliant mind like yours.

2 MORGENHALL. Yes. Thank God. It's very brilliant.

3 FOWLE. And all that training.

4 MORGENHALL. Years of it. Hard, hard training.

5 FOWLE. You'll solve it, sir.

Thoughtful silence.

6 MORGENHALL. Fowle. Do you know what I've heard Tuppy Morgan say? After all, he's sat here, year in, year out, as long as anyone can remember, in Court, waiting for the Dock Brief himself. Wilfred, he's frequently told me, if they ever give you a brief, old fellow, attack the medical evidence. Remember, the jury's full of rheumatism and arthritis and shocking gastric troubles. They love to see a medical man put through it. Always go for a doctor.

7 FOWLE [*eagerly*]. You'd like to try?

8 MORGENHALL. Shall we?

9 FOWLE. I'd enjoy it.

10 MORGENHALL. Doctor. Did you say the lady died of heart failure?

11 FOWLE [*as* DOCTOR]. No.

12 MORGENHALL. Come doctor. Don't fence with me. Her heart wasn't normal when you examined her, was it?

13 FOWLE. She was dead.

14 MORGENHALL. *So* it had stopped.

15 FOWLE. Yes.

16 MORGENHALL. Then her heart had failed?

17 FOWLE. Well . . .

18 MORGENHALL. So she died of heart failure?

19 FOWLE. But . . .

20 MORGENHALL. And heart failure might have been brought on by a fit, I say a fit of laughter, at a curiously rich joke on the wireless?

1 FOWLE. Whew.

    FOWLE *claps softly.*

2 MORGENHALL. Thank you, Fowle. It was kind but, I thought, hollow. I don't believe my attack on the doctor was convincing.

3 FOWLE. Perhaps a bit unlikely. But clever. . . .

4 MORGENHALL. Too clever. No. We're not going to win this on science, Fowle. Science must be thrown away. As I asked those questions, I saw I wasn't even convincing you of your own innocence. But you respond to emotion, Fowle, as I do, the magic of oratory, the wonderful power of words.

5 FOWLE. Now you're talking.

6 MORGENHALL. I'm going to talk.

7 FOWLE. I wish I could hear some of it. Words as grand as print.

8 MORGENHALL. A golden tongue. A voice like a lyre to charm you out of hell.

9 FOWLE. Now you've commenced to wander away from all I've understood.

10 MORGENHALL. I was drawing on the riches of my classical education which comforts me on buses, waiting at surgeries, or in prison cells. But I shall speak to the jury simply, without classical allusions. I shall say. . . .

11 FOWLE. Yes.

12 MORGENHALL. I shall say . . .

13 FOWLE. What?

14 MORGENHALL. I had it on the tip of my tongue.

15 FOWLE. Oh.

16 MORGENHALL. I shan't disappoint you. I shall speak for a day, perhaps two days. At the end I shall say. . .

17 FOWLE. Yes. Just the closing words.

18 MORGENHALL. The closing words.

1 FOWLE. To clinch the argument.

2 MORGENHALL. Yes. The final, irrefutable argument.

3 FOWLE. If I could only hear.

4 MORGENHALL. You shall, Fowle. You shall hear it. In Court. It'll come out in Court, and when I sink back in my seat, trembling, and wipe the real tears off my glasses....

5 FOWLE. The judge's summing up.

6 MORGENHALL. What will Tommy say?

7 FOWLE [as JUDGE]. Members of the jury. . . .

8 MORGENHALL. Struggling with emotion as well.

9 FOWLE. I can't add anything to the words of the barrister. Go out and consider your verdict.

10 MORGENHALL. Have they left the box?

11 FOWLE. Only a formality.

12 MORGENHALL. I see. I wonder how long they'll be out [Pause.] They're out a long time.

13 FOWLE. Of course, it must seem long to you. The suspense.

14 MORGENHALL. I hope they won't disagree.

15 FOWLE. I don't see how they can.

Pause.

16 MORGENHALL. Fowle.

17 FOWLE. Yes, sir.

18 MORGENHALL. Shall we just take a peep into the jury room?

19 FOWLE. I wish we could.

20 MORGENHALL. Let's. Let me see, you're the foreman?

21 FOWLE [as FOREMAN]. I take it we're all agreed, chaps. So let's sit here and have a short smoke.

22 MORGENHALL [as a MEMBER OF THE JURY]. An excellent idea. The barrister saved him.

1 FOWLE. That wonderful speech. I had a bit of doubt before I heard the speech.

2 MORGENHALL. No doubt now, have you?

3 FOWLE. Certainly not. [*Pause.*] Care for a fill of mine?

4 MORGENHALL. Thank you so much. Match?

5 FOWLE. Here you are.

6 MORGENHALL. I say, you don't think the poor fellow's in any doubt, do you?

7 FOWLE. No. He must know he'll get off. After the speech I mean.

8 MORGENHALL. I mean, I wouldn't like him to be on pins....

9 FOWLE. Think we ought to go back and reassure him?

10 MORGENHALL. As you wish. Careful that pipe doesn't start a fire in your pocket. [*As* CLERK OF COURT.] Gentlemen of the jury. Have you considered your verdict?

11 FOWLE. We have.

12 MORGENHALL. And do you find the prisoner guilty or not guilty?

13 FOWLE. Not guilty, my Lord.

14 MORGENHALL. Hooray!

15 FOWLE [*as* JUDGE]. Now, if there's any sort of Mafeking around, I'll have the court closed.

16 MORGENHALL. So I'm surrounded, mobbed. Tuppy Morgan wrings my hand and says it was lucky he left the seat. The judge sends me a letter of congratulation. The journalists dart off to their little telephones. And what now: 'Of course they'd make you a judge but you're probably too busy . . .' There's a queue of solicitors on the stairs . . . My old clerk writes on my next brief, a thousand guineas to divorce a duchess. There are questions of new clothes, laying down the port. Oh, Mr. Fowle, the change in life you've brought me.

17 FOWLE. It will be your greatest day.

1 MORGENHALL. Yes, Mr. Fowle. My greatest day.

The bolts shoot back, the door opens slowly.

2 MORGENHALL. What's that? I said we weren't to be interrupted. It's draughty in here with that door open. Close it, there's a good chap, do.

3 FOWLE. I think, you know, they must want us for the trial.

Fade out.

Music.

Fade in the cell door opening.

4 MORGENHALL. He's not here at the moment—he's not . . . ? Oh, I'm so glad. Just out temporarily? With the governor? Then, I'll wait for him. Poor soul. How's he taking it? You're not allowed to answer questions? The regulations, I suppose. Well, you must obey the regulations. I'll just sit down here, and wait for Mr. Fowle.

The door closes. MORGENHALL *whistles. His whistling stops.*

5 MORGENHALL. May it please you, my Lord, *members* of the jury. I should have said, may it please you, my *Lord,* members of the jury. I should have said . . . [*He begins to walk up and down.*] Members of the jury. Is there one of you who doesn't crave for peace . . . crave for peace. The silence of an undisturbed life, the dignity of an existence without dependents . . . without jokes. Have you never been tempted?
I should have said . . .
Members of the *jury.* You and I are men of the world. If your Lordship would kindly not interrupt my speech to the jury. I'm obliged. Members of the jury, before I was so rudely interrupted . . . I might have said. . . . Look at the prisoner, members of the jury. Has he hurt you, done you the slightest harm? Is he not the mildest of men? He merely took it upon himself to regulate his

domestic affairs. An Englishman's home is his castle. Do any of you feel a primitive urge, members of the jury, to be revenged on this gentle bird fancier. . . .

Members of the jury, I see I'm affecting your emotions, but let us consider the weight of the evidence. . . .

Might have said that!

I might have said . . . [*With distress.*] I might have said something. . . .

The door opens.

2 FOWLE. I was hoping you'd find time to drop in, sir. I'm afraid you're upset.

3 MORGENHALL. No, no, my dear chap. Not at all, upset.

4 FOWLE. The result of the trial's upset you.

5 MORGENHALL. I feel a little dashed. A little out of sorts.

6 FOWLE. It was disappointing for you.

7 MORGENHALL. A touch of disappointment. But there'll be other cases. There may be other cases.

8 FOWLE. But you'd built such high hopes on this particular one.

9 MORGENHALL. Well, there it is, Fowle.

10 FOWLE. It doesn't do to expect too much of a particular thing.

11 MORGENHALL. You're right, of course.

12 FOWLE. Year after year I used to look forward keenly to the feathered friends fanciers' annual do. Invariably it took the form of a dinner.

13 MORGENHALL. Your yearly treat?

14 FOWLE. Exactly. All I had in the enjoyment line. Each year I built high hopes on it. June 13th, I'd say, now there's an evening to look forward to.

15 MORGENHALL. Something to live for?

16 FOWLE. In a way. But when it came, you know, it was never up to it. Your collar was always too tight, or the food was inadequate, or someone had a nasty scene with the

fancier in the chair. So, on June 14th, I always said to myself: Thank God for a night at home.

2 MORGENHALL. It came and went and your life didn't change?

3 FOWLE. No, quite frankly.

4 MORGENHALL. And this case has left me just as I was before.

5 FOWLE. Don't say that.

6 MORGENHALL. Tuppy Morgan's back in his old seat under the window. The judge never congratulated me. No one's rung up to offer me a brief. I thought my old clerk looked coldly at me, and there was a titter in the luncheon room when I ordered my usual roll and tomato soup.

7 FOWLE. But I. . . .

8 MORGENHALL. And you're not left in a very favourable position.

9 FOWLE. Don't say that, sir. It's not so bad for me. After all, I had no education.

10 MORGENHALL. So many years before I could master the Roman Law relating to the ownership of chariots. . . .

11 FOWLE. Wasted, you think?

12 MORGENHALL. I feel so.

13 FOWLE. But without that rich background, would an individual have been able to sway the Court as you did?

14 MORGENHALL. Sway?

15 FOWLE. The Court.

16 MORGENHALL. Did I do that?

17 FOWLE. It struck me you did.

18 MORGENHALL. Indeed. . . .

19 FOWLE. It's turned out masterly.

20 MORGENHALL. Mr. Fowle, you're trying to be kind. When I was a child I played French cricket with an uncle who deliberately allowed the ball to strike his legs. At the age of seven that irked me. At sixty-three I can face the difficulties of accurate batting. . . .

1 FOWLE. But no, sir. I really mean it. I owe it all to you. Where I am.

2 MORGENHALL. I'm afraid near the end.

3 FOWLE. Just commencing.

4 MORGENHALL. I lost, Mr. Fowle. You may not be aware of it. It may not have been hammered home to you yet. But your case is lost.

5 FOWLE. But there are ways and ways of losing.

6 MORGENHALL. That's true, of course.

7 FOWLE. I noticed your artfulness right at the start, when the policeman gave evidence. You pulled out that red handkerchief, slowly and deliberately, like a conjuring trick.

8 MORGENHALL. And blew?

9 FOWLE. A sad, terrible trumpet.

10 MORGENHALL. Unnerved him, I thought.

11 FOWLE. He never recovered. There was no call to ask questions after that.

12 MORGENHALL. And then they called that doctor.

13 FOWLE. You were right not to bother with him.

14 MORGENHALL. Tactics, you see. We'd decided not to trouble with science.

15 FOWLE. So we had. And with Bateson. . . .

16 MORGENHALL. No, Fowle. I must beware of your flattery, I think I might have asked Bateson. . . .

17 FOWLE. It wouldn't have made a farthing's difference. A glance told them he was a demon.

18 MORGENHALL. He stood there, so big and red, with his no tie and dirty collar. I rose up to question him and suddenly it seemed as if there were no reason for us to converse. I remembered what you said about his jokes, his familiarity with your wife. What had he and I in common? I turned from him in disgust. I think that jury guessed the reason for my silence with friend Bateson.

1 FOWLE. I think they did!

2 MORGENHALL. But when it came to the speech. . . .

3 FOWLE. The best stroke of all.

4 MORGENHALL. I can't agree. You no longer carry me with you.

5 FOWLE. Said from the heart.

6 MORGENHALL. I'm sure of it. But not, dare I say, altogether justified? We can't pretend, can we, Mr. Fowle, that the speech was a success?

7 FOWLE. It won the day.

8 MORGENHALL. I beg you not to be under any illusions. They found you guilty.

9 FOWLE. I was forgetting. But that masterly speech. . . .

10 MORGENHALL. I can't be hoodwinked.

11 FOWLE. But you don't know. . . .

12 MORGENHALL. I stood up, Mr. Fowle, and it was the moment I'd waited for. Ambition had driven me to it, the moment when I was alone with what I wanted. Everyone turned to me, twelve blank faces in the jury box eager to have the grumpy looks wiped off them. The judge was silent. The prosecutor courteously pretended to be asleep. I only had to open my mouth and pour words out. What stopped me?

13 FOWLE. What?

14 MORGENHALL. Fear. That's what's suggested. That's what the clerks tittered to the waitresses in Friday's luncheon room. Old Wilf Morgenhall was in a funk.

15 FOWLE. More shame on them. . . .

16 MORGENHALL. But it wasn't so. Nor did my mind go blank. When I rose I knew exactly what I was going to say.

17 FOWLE. Then, why?

18 MORGENHALL. Not say it—you were going to say?

19 FOWLE. It had struck me—

1 MORGENHALL. It must have, Fowle. It must have struck many people. You'll forgive a reminiscence. . . .

2 FOWLE. Glad of one.

3 MORGENHALL. The lady I happened to mention yesterday. I don't of course, often speak of her. . . .

4 FOWLE. She, who, in the 1914. . . . ?

5 MORGENHALL. Exactly. But I lost her long before that. For years, you know, Mr. Fowle, this particular lady and I met at tea parties, tennis, and so on. Then, one evening I walked home with her. We stood on Vauxhall Bridge, a warm summer night, and silence fell. It was the moment when I should have spoken, the obvious moment. Then, something overcame me, It wasn't shyness or fear then, but a tremendous exhaustion. I was tired out by the long wait, and when the opportunity came—all I could think of was sleep.

6 FOWLE. It's a relief. . . .

7 MORGENHALL. To go home alone. To undress, clean your teeth, knock out your pipe, not to bother with failure or success.

8 FOWLE. So yesterday. . . .

9 MORGENHALL. I had lived through that moment so many times. It happened every day in my mind, daydreaming on buses, or in the doctor's surgery. When it came I was tired of it. The exhaustion came over me. I wanted it to be all over. I wanted to be alone in my room, in the darkness, with a soft pillow round my ears. . . . So I failed.

10 FOWLE. Don't say it.

11 MORGENHALL. Being too tired to make my daydream public. It's a nice day. Summer's coming.

12 FOWLE. No, don't sir. Not too near the window.

13 MORGENHALL. Why not, Mr. Fowle?

14 FOWLE. I was concerned. A man in your position might be desperate. . . .

1   MORGENHALL. You say you can see the forest?

2   FOWLE. Just a splash of it.

3   MORGENHALL. I think I shall retire from the bar.

4   FOWLE. Don't say it, sir. After that rigorous training.

5   MORGENHALL. Well, there it is. I think I shall retire.

6   FOWLE. But cheer up, sir. As you said, other cases, other days. Let's take this calmly, sir. Let's be very lucid, as you put it in your own statement.

7   MORGENHALL. Other cases? I'm getting on, you know. Tuppy Morgan's back in his place. I doubt if the Dock brief will come round again.

8   FOWLE. But there'll be something.

9   MORGENHALL. What can there be? Unless?

10 FOWLE. Yes, sir?

11 MORGENHALL. There would be another brief if. . . .

12 FOWLE. Yes?

13 MORGENHALL. I advised you to appeal. . . .

14 FOWLE. Ah, now that, misfortunately. . . .

15 MORGENHALL. There's a different atmosphere there, up in the Appeal Court, Fowle. It's far from the rough and tumble, question and answer, swear on the Bible and lie your way out of it. It's quiet up there, pure Law, of course. Yes. I believe I'm cut out for the Court of Appeal. . . .

16 FOWLE. But you see. . . .

17 MORGENHALL. A big, quiet Court in the early Summer afternoon. Piles of books, and when you put one down the dust and powdered leather rises and makes the ushers sneeze. The clock ticks. Three old judges in scarlet take snuff with trembling hands. You'll sit in the dock and not follow a legal word. And I'll give them all my Law and get you off on a technicality.

18 FOWLE. But today. . . .

1 MORGENHALL. Now, if I may remind your Lordships of Prickle against the Haverfordwest Justices ex parte Anger, reported in 96 Moor's Ecclesiastical at page a thousand and three. Have your Lordships the report? Lord Bradwell, C. J., says, at the foot of the page. 'The guilty intention is a deep foundation stone in the wall of our jurisprudence. So if it be that Prickle did run the bailiff through with his poignard taking him for a stray dog or cat, it seems there would be well raised the plea of autrefois mistake. But, contra, if he thought him to be his neighbour's cat, then, as my Brother Breadwinkle has well said in Lord Roche and Anderson, there might fall out a constructive larceny and felo in rem.' Oh, Mr. Fowle, I have some of these fine cases by heart.

2 FOWLE. Above me, I'm afraid, you're going now.

3 MORGENHALL. Of course I am. These cases always bore the prisoner until they're upheld or overruled and he comes out dead or alive at the end of it all.

4 FOWLE. I'd like to hear you reading them, though. . . .

5 MORGENHALL. You would. I'll be followed to Court by my Clerk, an old tortoise burdened by the weight of authorities. Then he'll lay them out in a fine buff and half cow row, a letter from a clergyman I correspond with in Wales torn to mark each place. A glass of water, a dry cough and the 'My respectful submission.'

6 FOWLE. And that, of course, is. . . .

7 MORGENHALL. That the judge misdirected himself. He forgot the rule in Rimmer's case, he confused his mens sana, he displaced the burden of proof, he played fast and loose with all reasonable doubt, he kicked the presumption of innocence round like a football.

8 FOWLE. Strong words.

9 MORGENHALL. I shan't let Tommy Banter off lightly.

10 FOWLE. The judge?

11 MORGENHALL. Thoroughly unscholarly. Not a word of Latin in the whole summing up.

1   FOWLE. Not up to you, of course.

2   MORGENHALL. Thank God, I kept my books. There have been times, Fowle, when I was tempted, pricked and harried for rent perhaps, to have my clerk barter the whole lot away for a few pounds they offer for centuries of entombed law. But I stuck to them. I still have my Swabey and Tristram, my Pod's Privy Council, my Spinks Prize Cases. I shall open them up and say . . . I shall say. . . .

3   FOWLE. It's no good.

4   MORGENHALL. What's no good?

5   FOWLE. It's no good appealing.

6   MORGENHALL. No good?

7   FOWLE. No good at all.

8   MORGENHALL. Mr. Fowle. I've worked hard for you.

9   FOWLE. True enough.

10   MORGENHALL. And I mean to go on working.

11   FOWLE. It's a great comfort. . . .

12   MORGENHALL. In the course of our close, and may I say it? yes, our happy collaboration on this little crime of yours, I've become almost fond of you.

13   FOWLE. Thank you, sir.

14   MORGENHALL. A first, I have to admit it, I was put off by your somewhat furtive and repulsive appearance. It's happened before. I saw, I quite agree, only the outer husk, and what I saw was a small man marked by all the physical signs of confirmed criminality.

15   FOWLE. No oil painting?

16   MORGENHALL. Let's agree on that at once.

17   FOWLE. The wife thought so, too.

18   MORGENHALL. Enough of her, poor woman.

19   FOWLE. Oh, agreed.

20   MORGENHALL. My first solicitude for your well-being, let's face up to this as well, had a selfish element. You were my very own case, and I didn't want to lose you.

1   FOWLE. Natural feelings. But still. . . .

2   MORGENHALL. I haven't wounded you?

3   FOWLE. Nothing fatal.

4   MORGENHALL. I'm glad. Because, you know, as we worked on this case together, an affection sprang up. . . .

5   FOWLE. Mutual.

6   MORGENHALL. You seemed to have a real desire to help, and, if I may say so, an instinctive taste for the law.

7   FOWLE. A man can't go through this sort of thing without getting legal interests.

8   MORGENHALL. Quite so. And of course, as a self-made man, that's to your credit. But I did notice, just at the start, some flaws in you as a client.

9   FOWLE. Flaws?

10 MORGENHALL. You may not care to admit it. But let's be honest. After all, we don't want to look on the dreary side; but you may not be with us for very long. . . .

11 FOWLE. That's what I was trying to say. . . .

12 MORGENHALL. Please, Mr. Fowle, no interruptions until we've cleared this out of the way. Now didn't you, just at the beginning, put unnecessary difficulties before us?

13 FOWLE. Did I?

14 MORGENHALL. I well remember, before I got a bit of keenness into you, that you seemed about to admit your guilt.

15 FOWLE. Oh. . . .

16 MORGENHALL. Just a little obstinate, wasn't it?

17 FOWLE. I dare say. . . .

18 MORGENHALL. And now, when I've worked for fifty years to get the Law at my finger-tips, I hear you mutter, 'No appeal.'

19 FOWLE. No appeal!

20 MORGENHALL. Mr. Fowle. . . .

21 FOWLE. Yesterday you asked me to spare you pain, sir. This is going to be very hard for me.

1   MORGENHALL. What?

2   FOWLE. As you say, we've worked together, and I've had the pleasure of watching the ticking over of a legal mind. If you'd call any afternoon I'd be pleased to repay the compliment by showing you my birds. . . .

3   MORGENHALL. Not in this world you must realize, unless we appeal.

4   FOWLE. You see, this morning I saw the Governor.

5   MORGENHALL. You had some complaint?

6   FOWLE. I don't want to boast, but the truth is . . . he sent for me.

7   MORGENHALL. You went in fear. . . .

8   FOWLE. And trembling. But he turned out a very gentlemanly sort of individual. Ex-Army, I should imagine. All the ornaments of a gentleman. Wife and children in a tinted photo framed on the desk, handsome oil painting of a prize pig over the mantelpiece. Healthy red face. Strong smell of scented soap. . . .

9   MORGENHALL. But grow to the point. . . .

10   FOWLE. I'm telling you. 'Well, Fowle' he says, 'Sit down do. I'm just finishing this letter.' So I sat and looked out of his windows. Big wide windows in the Governor's office, and the view. . . .

11   MORGENHALL. Fowle. If this anecdote has any point, be a good little chap, reach it.

12   FOWLE. Of course it has, where was I?

13   MORGENHALL. Admiring the view as usual.

14   FOWLE. Panoramic it was. Well, this Governor individual finishing his letter, lit up one of those flat type of Egyptian cigarettes. 'Well, Fowle,' he said. . . .

15   MORGENHALL. Yes, yes. It's not necessary, Fowle, to reproduce every word of this conversation. Give us the gist, just the meat, you understand. Leave out the trimmings.

16   FOWLE. Trimmings there weren't. He put it quite bluntly.

1   MORGENHALL. What did he put?

2   FOWLE. 'Well, Fowle, this may surprise you. But the Home Office was on the telephone about you this morning.' Isn't that a Government department?

3   MORGENHALL. Yes, yes, and well. . . .

4   FOWLE. It seems they do, in his words, come through from time to time, and just on business, of course, on that blower. And quite frankly, he admitted he was as shocked as I was. But the drill is, as he phrased it, a reprieve.

5   MORGENHALL. A. . . ?

6   FOWLE. It's all over. I'm free. It seems that trial was no good at all. . . .

7   MORGENHALL. No good. But why?

8   FOWLE. Oh, no particular reason.

9   MORGENHALL. There must be a reason. Nothing passes in the Law without a reason.

10 FOWLE. You won't care to know.

11 MORGENHALL. Tell me.

12 FOWLE. You're too busy to wait. . . .

13 MORGENHALL. Tell me, Mr. Fowle. I beg you. Tell me directly why this Governor, who knows nothing about the Law, should have called our one and only trial together 'No good.'

14 FOWLE. You yourself taught me not to scatter information like bombs.

15 MORGENHALL. Mr. Fowle. You must answer my question. My legal career may depend upon it. If I'm not to have wasted my life on useless trials.

16 FOWLE. You want to hear?

17 MORGENHALL. Certainly.

18 FOWLE. He may not have been serious. There was a twinkle, most likely, in his eye. . . .

19 MORGENHALL. But he said. . . .

1 FOWLE. That the barrister they chose for me was no good. An old crock, in his words. No good at all. That he never said a word in my defence. So my case never got to the jury. He said the whole business was ever so null and void, but I'd better be careful in the future. . . .

MORGENHALL *runs across the cell. Sounds as he mounts the stool.*

2 FOWLE. No! Mr. Morgenhall! Come down from there! No, sir! Don't do it!

Sounds of a struggle. The stool is upset and then put up again.

3 FOWLE. Don't you see? If I'd had a barrister who asked questions and made clever speeches I'd be as dead as mutton. Your artfulness saved me. . . .

4 MORGENHALL. My. . . .

5 FOWLE. The artful way you handled it. The dumb tactics. They paid off! I'm alive!

6 MORGENHALL. There is that. . . .

7 FOWLE. And so are you.

8 MORGENHALL. We both are?

9 FOWLE. I'm free.

10 MORGENHALL. To go back to your birds. I suppose. . . .

11 FOWLE. Yes, Mr. Morgenhall?

12 MORGENHALL. It's unlikely you'll marry again.

13 FOWLE. Unlikely.

Long pause.

14 MORGENHALL. But you have the clear appearance of a criminal. I suppose it's not impossible that you might commit some rather more trivial offence.

15 FOWLE. A man can't live, Mr. Morgenhall, without committing some trivial offences. Almost daily.

16 MORGENHALL. Then we may meet again. You may need my services. . . .

17 FOWLE. Constantly.

1 MORGENHALL. The future may not be so black. . . .

2 FOWLE. The sun's shining.

3 MORGENHALL. Can we go?

4 FOWLE. I think the door's been open some time. [*He tries it. It is unbolted and swings open.*] After you, Mr. Morgenhall. please.

5 MORGENHALL. No, no.

6 FOWLE. A man of your education should go first.

7 MORGENHALL. I think you should lead the way, Mr. Fowle, and as your legal adviser I will follow at a discreet distance, to straighten out such little tangles as you may hope to leave in your wake. Let's go.

MORGENHALL *whistles his fragment of tune.* FOWLE *joins in and they walk away down the corridor whistling together.*

Fade out

Don't Wait For Me

by David Campton

Cast:

A WAITRESS

LIZ

EDDIE

VIOLET

MRS. PARSONS

❉ ❉ ❉
Don't Wait For Me

Fade in the background sounds of a small café—a gentle tinkle of cups, and a discreet murmur of hushed voices.

The door opens, and there is a sudden burst of traffic noise from the street outside. The door is slammed shut.

LIZ breathes heavily—the wheezing pant of a fat woman, who has been hurrying. The panting becomes a sigh of relief as she sinks into a chair.

1   WAITRESS. I'm afraid you can't sit at the table by the window, madam.

2   LIZ. I'll have a cup of coffee.

3   WAITRESS. If you wouldn't mind moving.

4   LIZ. Strong, black, and without froth.

5   WAITRESS. I'll be glad to serve you at another table.

6   LIZ. You wouldn't be glad to serve me anywhere. I saw your face when I waltzed in. Dropped like an old sack. Make your customers proper welcome, don't you?

7   WAITRESS. We cater for a high class trade. Select people come for coffee in this café.

8   LIZ. I know what's wrong wi' you. You don't want anybody to peep through the window, and see me picking my nose. Might put 'em off. Know how long it is since I had a wash? Nor do I. I bet I stink. Where's that coffee?

9   WAITRESS. This table . . .

10   LIZ. Know where I've just come from? Court. Do you know what the beak did? Fined me for being drunk and disorderly. . . . 'You again?' His first words. 'You again!' he says. 'Floggin's too good for you, you drunken old baggage.' P'raps they weren't his exact words, but that's what he meant. So he fines me . . . Know what for? Aiming a pint pot at this barman. Missed him, though. Pity. But do you know why I threw that

jar? Do you?... He wouldn't serve me.... Cup of coffee. Please.

The door opens and shuts.

2 WAITRESS. Good morning, sir.

3 EDDIE. Oh. Good—good morning.

4 WAITRESS. Table for one, sir? Over in the corner.

5 EDDIE. I—er—I'll ... I'll sit here, if you don't mind. By the window.

6 WAITRESS. That seat is ...

7 EDDIE. Could I—. Would you bring me a cup of coffee? please.

8 WAITRESS [*sotto voice*]. Some people!

9 EDDIE. Liz ...

10 LIZ. You can't sit here. This table is reserved.

11 EDDIE. You didn't have to, you know. I mean—run away from me as if—as if ...

12 LIZ. I'm not in the habit of talking to strange men.

13 EDDIE. I—I thought I'd lost you. Then I saw you through this window.

14 LIZ. If a lady can't have a coffee without being accosted, I don't know what the place is coming to.

15 EDDIE. I was there. I heard ... They didn't give you half a chance. The magistrate didn't even listen.

16 LIZ. I can feel a draught. Somebody's mouth must be hanging open.

17 EDDIE. I shut up shop this morning. I went straight round to the Court as soon as I heard. I thought you might— sort of—need me. The fine, for instance. If you hadn't got enough for the fine, they might've locked you up.

18 LIZ. In a hole dead as this, there ought to be some peace and quiet.

19 EDDIE. I missed you on the way out. Different entrances.

1 LIZ. Is there a copper about? I've got a chap here making suggestions.

2 EDDIE. I only wanted to make sure that—that you were all right.

3 LIZ. Have you done forcing your attentions on me?

4 EDDIE. I'll—go. If you really want me to.

5 LIZ. Oh, sit where you are, you wet lump of tripe.

6 EDDIE. You admit that we know each other then?

7 LIZ. Well, if it isn't Eddie. Old Eddie George. . . . I'd sooner see the devil any day than your gormless mug.

There is a rattle of cups, ending with a thud as a tray is put on the table.

8 WAITRESS. Two coffees.

9 EDDIE. Oh—thanks.

10 WAITRESS. Enjoying the view?

11 LIZ. Sarky cat.

12 WAITRESS. Really!

13 LIZ. Pass the sugar. . . . Well, were you satisfied?

14 EDDIE. What with?

15 LIZ. The show. I saw you. In the public gallery, along with all the other old perishers. It's warm, dry and free. It was the first time for you, wasn't it? You missed all my other performances. The reporters like me, anyway. I liven their day up. 'Call Elizabeth Warton.' Laughter in Court. The beak said I could be done for contempt. Contempt! I'd have spit in his eye, only me mouth was like a sand pit. [*She takes a noisy sip of coffee.*] I hope you enjoyed yourself.

16 EDDIE. It was—hell. Stuck up there. Not being able to do anything—to help.

17 LIZ. Help?

18 EDDIE. That's why I followed you. I want. . . . You can't go on like this.

19 LIZ. Who says?

1   EDDIE. I want to do something for you. I mean—if only for old time's sake. It's daft—us both living in the same town and never. . . . It's not as if we'd ever quarrelled, or . . . I want to help.

2   LIZ. The only way anybody can help me is out of this world. I'm sick of it. I've tried long enough to fix myself with booze, only that's not strong enough. Do you think this coffee might do the trick? Smells as though the stuck-up cat mixed it with disinfectant. I'm worn out. Time I was traded in for a new model. . . . Don't stare like that or your eyes'll drop out. What's the matter wi' me? Tide mark showing?

3   EDDIE. You haven't changed, Liz. Not really. You haven't changed a bit. You're still the girl I—I . . .

4   LIZ. No, I'm not—so you can stop your goggling. Give me the flaming Willies. Reminding me where I've gone wrong.

5   EDDIE. Your hair . . .

6   LIZ. Hasn't been washed for years. And my beautiful blue eyes are bloodshot. I'm an old bag, and I don't need you to rub it in.

7   EDDIE. You're Liz.

8   LIZ. The girl you knew's been smothered under fifteen stone of fat. If you don't recognize that you're softer than I took you for. Drink your coffee, and get out.

9   EDDIE. Do you know what this place is? Do you?

10   LIZ. Don't you try to make me sorry for myself. I deserved all I got.

11   EDDIE. This is the place where I—first met you.

12   LIZ. Don't be gormless. It hasn't been built more than a couple of years.

13   EDDIE. It was—open ground then. The town had hardly pushed out this far. You must remember.

14   LIZ. Are you trying to make my flesh creep?

1   EDDIE. There was a—bit of a brook. It ran just about where those tables are now. They must have—what d'you call it—pushed it out of the way—diverted it. And there were trees.

2   LIZ. Shut up, will you? You're worse than a hangover. Shut up.

3   EDDIE. It was a Sunday afternoon.

4   LIZ. What was?

5   EDDIE. When I met you.

6   LIZ. I knew you'd be off like this. I kept out of your way while I could.

7   EDDIE. Not long after the Great War it would be. Not more than a few years, anyway. About 1920.

8   LIZ. Slobber, slobber, slobber.

9   EDDIE. You wouldn't have been more than sixteen. With funny long skirts, and your hair flying wild.

10   LIZ. If you don't give over, I'll let you have this coffee. Straight between the eyes.

11   EDDIE. I was only trying to—remind you.

12   LIZ. You're making me sick. Counting cherry stones. Picking daisy petals. You needn't trouble yourself: I can give you the answer now. It's 'she loves me not'.

13   EDDIE. Forty years ago. Here. Right here.

14   LIZ. It don't do any good to remember.

The background noise of the café fades out.

15   EDDIE [*in a whisper*]. There was a girl with you—what was her name?

16   LIZ. Leave me out of it.

17   VI [*calling from a distance*]. Elizabeth.

18   EDDIE. Vi. That's it. Vi. A funny kid. Almost old enough, but not quite.

19   VI [*still distant*]. Liz. Liz.

20   EDDIE. She had pink ribbon in her hair.

1   LIZ. Blue.

    EDDIE *forces* LIZ *to remember the past. A bird sings in a nearby tree and children can be heard playing in the distance.*

2   EDDIE. And she was looking for you.

3   VI [*approaching*]. Liz. Liz. Elizabeth. I'm calling you.

4   EDDIE [*now eighteen*]. Can I . . .

5   VI [*gives a little shriek*].

6   EDDIE [*lamely*]. Do anything for you?

7   VI. No. No, you can't.

8   EDDIE. I—didn't frighten you, did I? I heard you calling.

9   VI. I wasn't calling for you.

10   EDDIE. I know. But I thought I . . .

11   VI. I'm sorry. I don't talk to strange boys. Elizabeth!

12   EDDIE. I didn't mean to . . .

13   VI [*retreating*]. Elizabeth. *Elizabeth!*

14   EDDIE. Please . . .

    LIZ *laughs. Her voice has lost its fog and gin rasp. It, too, is lighter. In fact,* LIZ *is quite a different person.*

15   EDDIE. Who . . . ?

16   LIZ [*now fifteen*]. I was watching from behind yon tree . . . 'I don't talk to strange boys.' . . . She tries to make sure that *I* don't either. That's why I dodged her.

17   EDDIE. Are you Elizabeth?

18   LIZ. I had my eye on you. You were sitting behind that bush. Reading.

19   EDDIE. Yes.

20   LIZ. Why?

21   EDDIE. I like—reading.

22   LIZ. Oh. . . . What does it say? . . . Go on. Read us a bit. . . . What were you reading just then?

23   EDDIE. I—er. Well . . . 'She cannot fade, though thou hast not thy bliss. For ever wilt thou love, and she be fair.'

1 LIZ. What does that mean?

2 EDDIE. I don't know.

3 LIZ. Strikes me you're a bit of a gorm.

4 EDDIE. I suppose I am.

5 LIZ. How old are you?

6 EDDIE. Eighteen.

7 LIZ. What's your name?

8 EDDIE. Eddie. Eddie George.

9 LIZ. What do you do?

10 EDDIE. Work in the shoe shop.

11 LIZ. Ever been out with a girl?

12 EDDIE. No.

13 LIZ. Sooner sit reading?

14 EDDIE. No.

15 LIZ. Bet you think I've got a cheek. All them questions.

16 EDDIE. No, I think . . . I think . . .

17 LIZ. What?

18 EDDIE. You're pretty.

19 LIZ. Think so?

20 EDDIE. Nice hair, and—and you've got blue eyes.

21 LIZ. I wish you didn't sound so daft when you said that.

22 EDDIE. I meant it.

23 LIZ. Did you? You're not so bad looking yourself. Pity you're so slow.

24 EDDIE. I—can't help that—I suppose.

25 LIZ. Want to know something? I've never talked to a strange lad before. I did it for a dare. Our mam says that I mustn't talk to strange lads. She says you never know what might happen. She told me to keep away from the bushes on the reccy, too. But I didn't, did I? I wanted to see what would happen. Only nothing happened, did it?

1   EDDIE. Yes.

2   LIZ. What happened?

3   EDDIE. I can't say—but. . . . Something happened. To me.

4   LIZ. You might look muck-struck, but you're nice. I think we could get on together. Pity I only started talking to make Vi mad.

5   VI [*distant*]. Liz. Liz. Elizabeth.

6   LIZ. I'm going to make her madder.

7   VI [*approaching, breathless*]. It's not fair, making me run after you. Your mother wouldn't like it if she . . . [*She stops, and continues primly.*] We had better be going.

8   LIZ. You're not scared, are you? Not of him.

9   VI. He tried to—to. . . . He spoke to me.

10   LIZ. Well. I spoke to *him*, so that makes us evens. Anyway, he's harmless. Aren't you? His name's Eddie, and he works in the shoe shop, and he's eighteen, and he's never. . . . And he's going to take me out next Sunday.

11   EDDIE [*faintly surprised at this information*]. Is he?

12   VI. You're fast, Elizabeth Warton. Fast. If you don't come home with me this minute, I'll—I'll tell your mother.

13   LIZ. I know you will. You can tell her something else an' all. Tell her you caught me kissing a strange lad behind bushes on reccy.

14   VI. You didn't!

15   LIZ. No, but I'm going to. . . . You don't mind, do you, Eddie? [*She gives him a kiss.*] There.

16   EDDIE. I can—do better than that. [*He gives her a kiss that takes her breath away.*]

17   VI. Stop it. I wouldn't have come out with you if I'd known you were going to carry on like this. We're supposed to be having a walk.

18   EDDIE. There!

19   LIZ [*breathless*]. Oh. [*Giggles softly.*] Oh.

20   VI. That's not nice.

1 LIZ. That's what you think.

2 VI. Your mother's going to hear all about this.

3 LIZ. She'll want to know what you were doing while it was going on.

4 VI. That's not fair.

5 LIZ. He's going to take me out next Sunday. Aren't you?

6 EDDIE. If you want me to.

7 LIZ. Let's see—we could bus it out as far as the locks. Then you could take me on the river.

8 EDDIE. I don't know about . . . I'll manage it—somehow.

9 LIZ. In a canoe, or a punt. I've never been in a punt before.

10 EDDIE. Nor have I.

11 VI. This is the last time I ever come out with you, Elizabeth Warton.

12 LIZ. He's got muscles up his arms. Come and feel his muscles. Vi.

13 VI. No.

14 LIZ. Muscles. I bet you're a devil with a punt pole.

15 VI. You swore! First it's boys, then it's bad language. I'm going straight home. When your mother sees me all alone, she's going to ask questions.

16 LIZ. The way you're going on, you'll never know the answers. You're only jealous. Give her a kiss, too, Eddie.

17 VI. No!

18 LIZ [*laughing*]. Go on.

19 VI [*retreating*]. I warned you!

    LIZ *laughs. The laugh ends a little uneasily.*

20 EDDIE. You're going to be in trouble.

21 LIZ. From our mam? Might give me the strap, that's all. She's very handy with the strap, is our mam.

1 EDDIE. Perhaps I . . . Should I go home with you—and explain?

2 LIZ. You? She'd slaughter you. I'm not old enough to go out with boys. Not sixteen till next August.

3 EDDIE. Oh, then you . . . Oh.

4 LIZ. What?

5 EDDIE. You—won't be coming out next Sunday.

6 LIZ. Did you think I was serious? About going on the river? . . . I thought you were just playing up with me. It was only meant to be a joke. I didn't know you'd take it serious.

7 EDDIE. No. Of course not.

8 LIZ. Would you really have taken me on the 'bus?

9 EDDIE. If you wanted.

10 LIZ. Just because I asked?

11 EDDIE. That's right.

12 LIZ. Now you make me feel a right ha'porth o' trash—me asking, and you taking me serious.

13 EDDIE. No. Of course not. I mean—I'd—do anything you asked.

14 LIZ. Would you? Why?

15 EDDIE. Because you're—you.

16 LIZ [giggling]. You don't mean it.

17 EDDIE. I do.

18 LIZ. You mean, if I—if I—asked you to—to jump in that brook, you'd go right ahead?

19 EDDIE. As long as it was you that asked.

20 LIZ. You'd get wet.

21 EDDIE. I'd do it.

22 LIZ. Very well, then. Go and jump in that brook. [Teasing.] Go on . . . I'm asking you.

23 EDDIE [suddenly]. All right.

There is a slight pause.

1 LIZ. Stop. Hey, stop. [*Alarmed.*] I asked you to stop. . . . You
would an' all. Can you beat it? Come back here. . . .
Come. . . . Please.

2 EDDIE [*approaching*]. Do you—believe me now?

3 LIZ. I wonder if you'd have stopped when you got to
the edge.

4 EDDIE. Do you want to try me?

5 LIZ. No!

6 EDDIE. You've only got to ask.

7 LIZ. You really want to take me out?

8 EDDIE. If you'll come.

9 LIZ. I'll come.

10 EDDIE. What about your mother—and . . .

11 LIZ. I said I'll come. But you can forget about the 'bus and
the river. Just a walk'll be enough. You can come a
bit of the way with me now if you like . . . Come on. . . .
As long as you stop when we get near home. You know,
I think I'm going to like you. You might easy be something special. [*Her voice recedes.*] Anything, you said. You'd
do anything.

Young LIZ *bursts into a peal of raucous laughter which mixes with
Liz's laughter ending in a bout of coughing.*

The café sounds return.

12 LIZ [*between wheezes*]. Ruddy fools. The pair of us. Is that the
memory you take to bed with you on cold winter
nights? The way you led me to ruin?

13 EDDIE. I didn't . . . We never . . .

14 LIZ. You showed me how I could twiddle a man around my
finger. At fifteen and a bit. Talk about games with
loaded guns.

15 EDDIE. It was—it was—a revelation.

16 LIZ. Letting a kid walk all over you. You'd have lain down
while I wiped my feet on your face.

1 EDDIE. I never believed such a thing could happen. Not to me.

2 LIZ. Slush. Turns me over inside to think. . . . Blast you for making me remember. To hell with you—may you rot where it's hottest. Damn. Damn . . .

3 EDDIE. Liz.

4 LIZ. What?

5 EDDIE. Will you marry me?

6 LIZ. Will? . . . A nut case!

7 EDDIE. I've not much to offer—never had.

8 LIZ. Anybody got a spare straight jacket?

9 EDDIE. Just that cobbler's shop, with a bit of a flat on top.

10 LIZ. The cuckoos are out late this year.

11 EDDIE. But it's yours—such as it is—if you want it.

12 LIZ. I'm not sitting here to be insulted.

13 EDDIE. Liz! It's—it's time you gave me a chance.

14 LIZ. I'm not myself this morning. If I were, I'd land you a smack where it matters. You and your suggestions.

15 EDDIE. Remember how we . . .

16 LIZ. I told you what you could do with your memories.

17 EDDIE. We could get on together. There's never been anybody else. Never.

18 LIZ. I've heard it all before.

19 EDDIE. It was here where I asked you the first time. Here.

20 LIZ. Wait while I stick my fingers in my ears.

The café background fades out.

21 EDDIE. I thought it was appropriate. The place where we met.

22 LIZ. How do they switch you off?

23 EDDIE. With the May Fair in full blast.

Far away the sound of a fairground organ creeps in.

1   EDDIE. Now or never, I thought. At the back of the round-abouts.

2   LIZ. What right have you to . . .

3   EDDIE. May, 1925.

4   LIZ. What's past is past. Bury it.

5   EDDIE. I'd already waited four years. You were nineteen, and looked a picture.

6   LIZ [*her voice rising to a shout*]. No! no! no! no! no!

The noise of the fairground organ bears down like an on-rushing monster, drowning LIZ's *protests. Then it retreats into the background again.*

7   LIZ [*the young* LIZ]. You were going to say?

8   EDDIE [*the young* EDDIE]. You've—sort of—grown up in the last couple of years.

9   LIZ. I'm a big girl now.

10   EDDIE. Taken to knocking about with all sorts of chaps.

11   LIZ. There's more than one sort of chap in this town. What one hasn't got, another has. I don't want to miss anything, that's all.

12   EDDIE. You—can't have missed much.

13   LIZ. Are you complaining?

14   EDDIE. No. I've—just noticed.

15   LIZ. You didn't drag me into the shadows just to tell me that, did you?

16   EDDIE. I—meant to say that—that sooner or later—you'll have to give up going round with so many chaps—and —settle down. With one.

17   LIZ. And—you've made up your mind who the one ought to be.

18   EDDIE. Yes.

19   LIZ. Is this—It?

20   EDDIE. You could—call it that.

21   LIZ. Oh.

22   EDDIE. Well?

1 LIZ. I—I often wondered how it might happen. I never thought of—back of the caravans; behind the round-abouts. . . . Are we going to see the Wall of Death? They say a fellow got killed there a couple of years back.

2 EDDIE. You're getting away from the question.

3 LIZ. Oh, yes. Getting wed.

4 EDDIE. Will you?

5 LIZ. There's something about you, Eddie—something any girl ought to jump at. You're kind, and thoughtful. You might only be a cobbler, but you're a gentleman. The girl who marries you won't have a thing to worry about.

6 EDDIE. You will then?

7 LIZ. No.

8 EDDIE. Oh.

9 LIZ. Did you expect me to say yes?

10 EDDIE. That was the idea. I've been saving.

11 LIZ. You haven't bought a ring, have you?

12 EDDIE. Not yet.

13 LIZ. That's a blessing. Though I suppose it might have done for your next girl.

14 EDDIE. There won't be a next girl. There couldn't be anybody else—after knowing you.

15 LIZ. I'm not all that special. You're worth ten of me, Eddie.

16 EDDIE. Then why—

17 LIZ. Don't go asking for reasons. It's too early, that's why. I'm nineteen. That's no age to be getting tied. You know what marriage means as well as I do. Sweating over a boiling stove with hands raw red from the washing water. Having kids, and ending with a figure like a suet pudding. Don't contradict me—I've seen my mam. All right, happen I'll come to it sooner or later,

but it's too soon yet. I don't need any lad to tell me what I look like—my mirror does that for me. It's not wrong, wanting what I've got to last a bit longer. Don't fret. You're one of the best, Eddie. If I had any sense, I wouldn't wait to be asked twice. Any other girl would have dragged you up the aisle years back. But I'm not ready yet to be locked in the kitchen. I've got to know what's round the corner. I don't want to hurt you. I'm not sure what love is—I can guess how it ought to feel, though—and I came closer to that with you than with anybody else. I'm a fool to say no, but . . .

2 EDDIE. Then don't say it. . . . Just say 'not yet'.

3 LIZ. That's hardly fair on you, is it?

4 EDDIE. I'll wait.

5 LIZ. I wouldn't advise it.

6 EDDIE. You're worth waiting for.

7 LIZ. I might go off in the end with a bloke in a big car. I've seen Arthur Kirby looking at me. He's got money to swim in. I might say 'yes' to a fur coat, and a house up The Lane.

8 EDDIE. I'll—take a risk.

9 LIZ. You're making it too easy for me. If only . . . Oh, go home.

10 EDDIE. But, Liz.

11 LIZ. Don't maul me.

12 EDDIE. Sorry, I—

13 LIZ. Go away.

14 EDDIE. If that's what you want . . .

15 LIZ. Leave me alone. Leave me alone. Would I ask if I didn't want? [*Her voice rises to a shout.*] Leave me. Leave me! Leave me!

The noise of the fair swells until it overwhelms her, then it is cut short, leaving the gentle noises of the café.

16 LIZ [*in a hoarse whisper*]. Leave me alone.

97

1 EDDIE. But, you see—I did wait.

2 LIZ. For what? Everybody else's leavings?

3 EDDIE. I wanted to—take care of you, Liz. I still do. Won't you let me? . . . You can't go on like this—booze all night, and magistrates in the morning. I can't—watch you sink.

4 LIZ. Nobody forces you.

5 EDDIE. Where's the next meal coming from?

6 LIZ. Where's the next drink coming from? That's more to the point. Feel like lending me a couple of quid?

7 EDDIE. I left a lump of shin o' beef in the pot—with onions and a bit of melt. I'll make dumplings when I get home. A plate of stew would do you good.

8 LIZ. I've been tempted with a fur coat before now, but never a plate of stew.

9 EDDIE. And there's a bed for you.

10 LIZ. Didn't take you long to get round to that, did it?

11 EDDIE. Well aired—with clean sheets and a new quilt. Any time you want it. And the bedroom's been fresh papered. I did it myself last spring. It's better than sleeping rough, isn't it?

12 LIZ. How did you know? You've been keeping your eyes open.

13 EDDIE. The nights are getting colder. How do you think it's going to end?

14 LIZ. With a funeral at the taxpayer's expense. And you still trailing after me, I suppose: a bunch of snowdrops in your hot little hand.

15 EDDIE. Wouldn't it be better for both of us if you were to marry me instead?

16 LIZ. It's not me you'll be mourning, though. It'll be that sharp-eyed little puss with the shining hair and the eighteen inch waist. You might save yourself the trouble, though. You said goodbye to her long enough since.

1 EDDIE. I never would. I knew there'd come a time when you
—wouldn't refuse.

2 LIZ. I might've married somebody else. I could have married
anybody—just by lifting a finger. In those days.

3 EDDIE. But you didn't.

4 LIZ. You had everything worked out. I was bound to end
neck-deep in the muck. Then there would be Eddie,
on his famous white horse to pull me clear. I had
everything worked out as well. We were both wrong.
[*She sniffs.*] They've started to cook dinner ... I can
smell the chips.

5 EDDIE. Would you like a meal here? I'll get it for you. We
can have the stew tomorrow.

6 LIZ. Chips. This place was a chip shop, before it was bombed
out.

The background of the café fades out.

They built it on the old reccy. Not far from the brook.
Where the fair used to pitch. This place used to be a
chip shop. You're not the only one who can remember.
Only I try to stop myself. Who wants to remember?
The chip pans were over there. Chromium weren't
they? With mirrors over the top. Chips. Nothing like the
smell for bringing back old times.... Why do you
let me go on?... It was a high class fish shop—used
white butcher's paper for wrapping instead of old
newspapers. Hygienic, but not so interesting.... I
don't want to remember.... There was a certificate
for something or other on the wall, and a big plate-glass
window, and—and—

7 MRS. PARSONS [*echo. Mumbling indistinctly*]. ... two separate
pennyworths, I said. You get more if you ask for
separate pennyworths. More than two pennyworth,
anyway. [*Her mumbling dies down.*]

8 LIZ. That old woman who talked to herself—who was she?
... Ma Parsons. Old Ma Parsons. Died years ago.

1 MRS. PARSONS [*echo*]. They warm you. Give your belly a lining. You've got to see that your belly's well lined.

2 LIZ. We always said she lived in a dog kennel. She was found one morning—frozen stiff.

3 MRS. PARSONS [*echo*]. Look after the inner man, I say. Let the outer man look after himself.

4 LIZ. And you were there, too, blast you. You were always there.

The sounds of a fish shop: a cash register, chips sizzling in oil, and customers talking in the background.

5 EDDIE [*young voice*]. Hello, Liz.

6 LIZ [*young voice*]. Why, Eddie ... Still waiting? I thought you might've given up.

7 EDDIE. You—don't really.

8 LIZ. I half-hoped you had.

9 MRS. PARSONS [*talking to herself as she does all the time*]. It's a hard life.

10 EDDIE. I don't see enough of you these days to—to miss a chance.

11 LIZ. Because I've got something to—that you ought to know.

12 MRS. PARSONS. You don't know what it's like when you're young.

13 EDDIE. Had we better ...

14 LIZ. She don't matter. She's not all here.

15 MRS. PARSONS. They make good chips, though.

16 LIZ. And nobody else is likely to come near while she's feeding. Let's move round a bit, then the wind'll be blowing the other way.

17 EDDIE. It's darker further down the street. There's—a bit too much light from the window.

18 LIZ. Don't bother yourself. We shan't be holding hands.

19 MRS. PARSONS. I eat 'em slow to make 'em last.

1   EDDIE. What was it you want to tell me?

2   LIZ. We've known each other a long time now.

3   EDDIE. Over ten years.

4   LIZ. Long enough to talk straight without beating about the bush.

5   EDDIE. Aye.

6   LIZ. I was twenty-six last birthday. It's time I was thinking about—my old age pension.

7   EDDIE. Liz! You've not. . . . Have you changed your mind?

8   LIZ. No.

9   MRS. PARSONS. I'm one of their best customers. And they know it.

10 LIZ. I've had an offer. You've met Arthur, haven't you? Arthur Kirby. You must have done. Drives all over the place in a big red sports car.

11 EDDIE. I might have seen the car.

12 LIZ. Runs that garage on the top of the hill. It's his own, you know. He put all his savings in it, and now he's making money so fast he doesn't know what to do with it all. At least—he's got ideas. He wants to spend some on me. The red sports job isn't his only car, you know. He's got two others. And a house of his own. He's having a tennis court built. . . . Well—it's him. He asked me.

13 MRS. PARSONS. Only they don't like me to hang about, because I put the other customers off.

14 EDDIE. He—wants to marry you.

15 LIZ. Not exactly. He's married already.

16 EDDIE. I thought you wanted. You won't be . . .

17 LIZ. As good as. He doesn't live with his wife. They never hit it off. She's an ailing thing. They never see each other.

18 EDDIE. Well, if it's—what you want.

19 LIZ. He'll do more for me than any other man in this town. How many do you know with a tennis court in their

back-yard? There isn't room to bounce a ball in ours.
Or yours. And he's got three cars. He's going to teach
me how to drive.

2 MRS. PARSONS. Sarky lot. I wouldn't give 'em my custom
only they make good chips.

3 LIZ. He's proper gone on me. He'd marry me like a shot, if
it wasn't for his wife.

4 EDDIE. Well . . . Congratulations.

5 LIZ. I'm never likely to do any better—three cars and a
tennis court.

6 EDDIE. I hope you'll—be happy.

7 LIZ. Who else do you know with three cars and a tennis
court?

8 MRS. PARSONS. Keep the cold out. Bitter wind these days.
Blows straight through.

9 EDDIE. You always wanted to get on.

10 LIZ. He's no more than ten years older than me, anyway.

11 EDDIE. I'd never be able to afford—even one car.

12 LIZ. And parties every weekend. The amount of whisky
that goes into that house. He only drinks heavy when
his leg hurts him, though. He had it broke up in the
war. His temper gets a bit short when his leg hurts him.
But he's an angel when it doesn't. When he does any
damage, he always apologises afterwards.

13 EDDIE. Can he play tennis with a bad leg?

14 LIZ. That doesn't matter. It's a sign you're getting on when
you can afford your own tennis court. He loses more
every week on the horses than you could earn. Every
week. And the things he's promised me. You'd be
surprised.

15 EDDIE. If it's what you want . . .

16 LIZ. Stop saying that. Of course it's not what I want. I want
a white wedding with bridesmaids and an organ, and a
ring on my third finger. But it's the best I'm likely to
get.—Three cars, and a tennis court.

1   MRS. PARSONS. You feel the weather when you get past seventy.

2   LIZ. I'm twenty-six, and making the most of what I'm blessed with.

3   MRS. PARSONS. You're only young once.

4   LIZ. What I wanted to tell you was—he's inclined to be jealous. He doesn't like the idea of other chaps—trespassing. He's liable to hit out.

5   EDDIE. After all—he's paying.

6   LIZ. You needn't be crude. . . . I—wouldn't want you to get mixed up in a fight over me, Eddie.

7   EDDIE. There's not much chance of that.

8   LIZ. I can't imagine you defying anybody.

9   EDDIE. I'm happy as long as you are.

10   LIZ. That's both of us satisfied, isn't it? So you'll have to fade out, as it were. We shan't be seeing so much of each other in the future.

11   EDDIE. I only want—what's best for you.

12   MRS. PARSONS. I wish I could afford a bob's worth. I'd stuff myself silly.

13   LIZ. It won't be long before you get married yourself, Eddie. You've got a lot to offer a girl.

14   EDDIE. None of it's what *you* want.

15   LIZ. You ought to try window dressing. Promise the moon. Give her the crown jewels to look forward to. Bed and breakfast is all very well, but there's no romance to it. Wouldn't you like to coax me away from Arthur?

16   EDDIE. He—he can't marry. I'll still wait.

17   LIZ. The most tempting offer I've heard yet.

18   EDDIE. Let them come and go. I'll still be here when the others have gone. You're going to marry me, Liz. You're going to marry me.

19   LIZ. Am I, Eddie?

20   EDDIE. I can wait.

1 LIZ [*flaring up*]. Then you'll wait for ever, you sloppy boob.
   And I'm warning you—stay out of my road when I'm
   driving.

She rushes out and slams the door behind her.

2 EDDIE. Liz!

3 MRS. PARSONS. The last of my chips. All gone. That's the
   way it is, more's the pity. Don't last.

4 EDDIE. You—you want looking after. Here. Get yourself
   something to eat. [*Following Liz through the door.*] Liz. Liz!

5 MRS. PARSONS. But it's—it's half a crown. Hey, you made a
   mistake young feller, it's . . . [*Chuckles to herself.*] I could—
   I could order all the chips in the pan, and eat, and eat...
   Or I could hang on to it, and have an extra pennyworth tomorrow. And the day after. It'll last longer
   in pennyworths. That's right. We'll make it last. Last.
   Last. Last . . . [*Her voice dies away on echo.*]

The café sounds fade in.

6 LIZ. Nothing lasts. Drink your coffee. Nothing lasts.

7 EDDIE. Don't say—nothing.

8 LIZ. I should have had my fortune told. Know what it
   would have said? Never trust a one-legged man when
   there's a depression in the month. Especially if he owns
   a garage, and a bankbook full of overdraft. He puts his
   head in the gas-oven, and me on the streets. And that
   was that. Still it was a beginning. There were plenty
   more after him. All shapes, sizes, and colours. And not
   one named Eddie.

9 EDDIE. I made a promise. Here I am.

10 LIZ. What am I supposed to do—cheer? You're no better
    than any of the others. You still want what they
    wanted. You're prepared to pay a different price, that's
    all. You're like the rest.

11 EDDIE. There's something—something special about me.
    I'm not—cracking myself up. It's just that—I know the

real Liz. I can remember what they can't—the girl who dared me to jump in the brook. Whatever happens—to me you'll always be that girl. Now, will you come home with me?

2   LIZ. Not if you were the last man in the world.

3   EDDIE. Why?

4   LIZ. Live with you, you great insensitive lump?

5   EDDIE. What—have I done?

6   LIZ. Done? You've made me ashamed of myself. Me. I thought shame and me were strangers. I can face up to any other chap—eye to eye—as brazen as they come. He can only see this, d'you see? This tousled mess. He can't tell what used to be. But you—you have to remind me—what might have been. The very sight of you makes me want to crawl into a hole, and hide. And why? Why? Because in your eyes there's still that fresh-faced cutie with the world at her feet. Live with you? I've got to live with *myself*. I'll have to go on the booze again tonight to take the taste of you out of my mind. . . . They walked home hand in hand—you and the girl who dared you to jump in the brook. Do me a favour, will you? Next time, make it the canal. Stay out of my sight. Permanent.

7   EDDIE. I want you, Liz.

8   LIZ. Not me. Not this bit of old filth. You wouldn't want this in your nice clean home. It wouldn't go with the new wallpaper.

9   EDDIE. You can't—run away from me again. You know how you'll end, don't you. Like Ma Parsons.

10   LIZ. That's about it.

11   EDDIE. All my life I've waited for you.

12   LIZ. You had your chances. Why didn't you take 'em?

13   EDDIE. Chances?

14   LIZ. The first time you asked me to marry you. The night I told you about Arthur.

1 EDDIE. You—didn't want . . .

2 LIZ. How do you know what I wanted?

3 EDDIE. You wouldn't . . .

4 LIZ. Then why didn't you make me? Why didn't you grab?
I wanted . . . [*Her voice recedes.*] Anyway, it's too late now.

The door opens and there is a sudden burst of street noise as she leaves.

5 EDDIE [*Shouting after her*]. Liz!

The door is slammed shut.

6 EDDIE. Liz.

7 WAITRESS. I really can't do with all that shouting. Give the
place a bad name. . . . Has she gone?

8 EDDIE. She's—gone.

9 WAITRESS. Oh. Then you'll be paying for both.

10 EDDIE. What? Oh. Oh, yes. I'd better pay for both of us.

The sounds of the café fade away.

She'll Make Trouble

by *Bill Naughton*

Cast:

THE GOVERNOR

CHIEF OFFICER JENKINS

MISS BARROWDALE-SMITH

OFFICER BURTON

RUTH LAWRENCE

OFFICER STONE

MRS. BUNN

MEDICAL ORDERLY

BLONDIE

CHIEF OFFICER MOONEY

ADA

OFFICER PRESTON

OFFICER SMITH

OFFICER BROWN

ADAMS

TILLOTSON

MEDICAL OFFICER

DAVIS

MRS. LAWRENCE

MR. LAWRENCE

OFFICER GREENHALSH

OFFICER LENEGAN

OFFICER MARTIN

OFFICER WILLIAMS

✳ ✳ ✳
She'll Make Trouble

The prison chapel. The choir is singing in the background.

1   GOVERNOR [*speaking over the choir*]. It was a bright morning in the prison chapel. The sun shone through the dark high slits of windows down on the prison choir, twelve men and twelve women. Between them a high screen shutting the men off from the women. Regulations: they're never allowed to see each other.

A tenor voice rises above the rest of the choir.

2   GOVERNOR. That's Tillotson, my tenor. Serving seven years for armed robbery. He couldn't sing a note when he first came in.

We now hear a bass voice singing solo.

3   GOVERNOR. That's Browitt, a bank manager. Doing five years for embezzling . . . and that baritone is Davis, burglar, six years. Then there's Fowler, twelve years preventive detention. Two in for manslaughter, another murderer, a bigamist and the rest burglars. It takes a long time to train a singer and that's why I've always got to depend on my long sentence people. Over on the women's side there, we have Maggie O'Casey, soprano, in for stabbing her lover, the Hon. Angela, contralto, a drug addict and false pretender. Lizzie Strickland, shoplifter, a receiver, a girl who poisoned her husband, a woman housebreaker, and others.

The singing comes to a stop.

4   GOVERNOR. Thank you, Choir, we're coming along nicely.

The door opens.

5   JENKINS. Excuse me, sir.

1 GOVERNOR. Yes, Chief Officer, what is it?

2 JENKINS. Telephone call for you, sir, Miss Barrowdale-Smith from Wensley Hill Women's Prison.

3 GOVERNOR. Thank you. Chief . . . !

4 JENKINS. Yes, sir?

5 GOVERNOR. Take over from me.

6 JENKINS. Me, sir! . . . Take over the choir! . . .

7 GOVERNOR. Yes . . . the last five minutes . . . thank you, Choir.

There are murmurs of unrest from the choir.

8 JENKINS [*Roars*]. Silence!

There is dead silence.

'And did those feet'. And if you don't mind we'll have the proper words. No passing messages.

The organ grunts, and we fade out on the choir singing.

'And did those feet in ancient times' . . .

Fade out.

A telephone is picked up.

9 GOVERNOR. Governor speaking.

10 MISS B-SMITH [*over the telephone*]. Miss Barrowdale-Smith here.

11 GOVERNOR. Sorry to keep you waiting, Smithy.

12 MISS B-SMITH. I just wanted to let you know that you're getting a woman transfer from here this morning.

13 GOVERNOR. Good, I could do with a new soprano.

14 MISS B-SMITH. She can sing. You'd hear her a mile away. Her name is Ruth Lawrence, in for larceny and what-not. Most difficult prisoner I've ever had to handle.

15 GOVERNOR. How old?

16 MISS B-SMITH. Nineteen.

1 GOVERNOR. Sounded like an old lag . . . !

2 MISS B-SMITH. Give me a prison-full of old lags before another Ruth.

3 GOVERNOR. Why did she ask to be transferred?

4 MISS B-SMITH. She didn't . . . We did. She had a real following here, and was turning the place upside-down.

5 GOVERNOR. You leave her to my Miss Mooney.

6 MISS B-SMITH. I've warned Miss Mooney—she didn't seem to take it seriously. I thought I'd tell you. She needs the heavy hand right from the start.

A car approaches outside.

7 GOVERNOR. I believe she's here now. Black saloon car.

8 MISS B-SMITH. That's her. With two of my officers. She's a fetching thing, but don't let that take you in. She'll make trouble. Goodbye.

9 GOVERNOR. Goodbye. [*He replaces the receiver. To himself.*] Mmm! . . . She's fetching!

Fade.

Fade in on the sound of handcuffs being unfastened. 3

10 OFFICER BURTON. I'll take the handcuffs.

11 RUTH. Thank you.

12 OFFICER BURTON. Goodbye, Ruth, do try and hold yourself in check a bit.

13 RUTH. I always do. It's when they bark at me I get mad.

14 OFFICER BURTON. Good luck.

15 RUTH. Thanks. Goodbye.

The sound of a food trolley approaching.

16 OFFICER STONE. Dinner! Put on your prison gowns. Back into your cubicles.

17 RUTH. Hi! Don't you shove me.

1   OFFICER STONE. You get inside your cubicle. You can't eat out here.

2   RUTH. I said, don't shove me.

3   OFFICER STONE. I'll see you later. Here's your dinner and get inside.

4   RUTH. Thank you very much. But don't shove. Ah, beef in a bundle. That drive made me hungry.

Sounds of eating. Mrs. Bunn can be heard sobbing.

5   RUTH. Hi . . . Psst! What's up with you?

Mrs. Bunn sobs.

6   RUTH. First time in?

7   MRS. BUNN. Yes . . .

8   RUTH. Eat up . . . you'll soon get used to it.

9   MRS. BUNN. I'll never get used . . .

10   RUTH. What have you got, twenty years?

11   MRS. BUNN. No . . . three months.

12   RUTH. Why, you'll be out in eight weeks.

13   MRS. BUNN. Ee, will I?

14   RUTH. A third off for good behaviour. So don't slosh anybody.

15   MRS. BUNN. I'd no idea I'd get sent to prison! I'll tell you what I did . . .

16   RUTH. Don't . . . unless you want to . . .

17   MRS. BUNN. I kept on drawing National Assistance after I'd got a cleaning job.

18   RUTH. No wonder the country's going bankrupt. Eat up, serve your bird, then leave with a good conscience.

19   MRS. BUNN [*cheered*]. Excuse me saying it . . . but if I saw you outside I'd never think you'd seen the inside of one of these places.

1   RUTH [put off step]. Oh . . . well . . . I've got to finish my dinner. I'm next after Blondie up there at Medical Reception.

2   MRS. BUNN. She is letting them have it isn't she?

Fade out.

Fade in. 4

3   BLONDIE. Verminous! What are you people trying to insinuate?

4   MEDICAL ORDERLY. You've never combed or brushed your hair for months.

5   BLONDIE. Would you comb a seven guinea perm out?

6   MEDICAL ORDERLY. Your head is verminous.

7   BLONDIE. Are you saying I've got nits or summink? I paid seven guineas for this little perm and bleach in Mayfair. What are you writing down?

8   MEDICAL ORDERLY. Verminous. Eaten in. Shave to scalp. Treat with Sassafaras.

9   BLONDIE. Wot—shave seven ruddy guineas worth away. Are you crazy? [Going off.] I demand to see the Governor . . .

10   OFFICER STONE [calls]. Next! Lawrence! Ruth Lawrence.

11   RUTH. Here.

12   OFFICER STONE. Step up here.

13   MEDICAL ORDERLY. Is your name Ruth Lawrence?

14   RUTH. Yes.

15   MEDICAL ORDERLY. Are you a transfer from Wensley Hill prison?

16   RUTH. I am. Have you washed your hands?

17   MEDICAL ORDERLY. Eh?

18   RUTH. You've just been handling Blondie.

19   OFFICER STONE. Here! . . . don't you speak to the medical orderly like that.

1 MEDICAL ORDERLY [*amused*]. She's right, Officer Stone. I'll go off and scrub up.

2 OFFICER STONE. You're one of the smart sort.

3 RUTH. I like things clean.

4 OFFICER STONE. Good. I'll supervise your bath. Don't forget we've tamed your sort before today . . .

Fade out.

Fade in. A knock on the door.

5 GOVERNOR. Come in. Yes, Jenkins?

6 JENKINS. Birmingham police on the phone, sir. They say they've picked up James Troddle. Detained him on suspicion.

7 GOVERNOR. He only went out yesterday!

8 JENKINS. That's him.

9 GOVERNOR. What are they holding him for?

10 JENKINS. Trying to sell a pair of boots and three pairs of socks, which they think were stolen.

11 GOVERNOR. Why ring us about it?

12 JENKINS. They'd all got Her Majesty's prison marked on them.

13 GOVERNOR. He knocked them off before leaving?

14 JENKINS. He'd hardly have broken into Birmingham gaol for them, sir.

15 GOVERNOR. But he said to me, 'I'll go straight from now on—I swear on my mother's life.'

16 JENKINS. That's his trouble, sir—he never had a mother!

17 GOVERNOR. What do they want from us?

The telephone rings.

18 JENKINS. Identification of articles.

THE GOVERNOR *lifts the receiver.*

1 GOVERNOR. Governor

2 MOONEY [*over the telephone*]. Are you coming over, sir?

3 GOVERNOR. Yes, later. Anything wrong?

4 MOONEY. Some trouble with the transfer, sir—Ruth Lawrence. She soaked an officer—during the admittance bath.

5 GOVERNOR. She's soon started. Is it a case for a magistrate?

6 MOONEY. I think you could handle it, sir.

7 GOVERNOR. I'll be right across. [*He replaces the telephone.*] Oh, Chief . . .

8 JENKINS. Yes, sir.

9 GOVERNOR. Think up something about those boots and socks.

10 JENKINS. I'd better, sir. Else we'll never live it down.

Fade out.

Fade in.   6

11 ADA. Miss Mooney, where shall I put the tea tray?

12 MOONEY. Thank you, Ada. On the table here. Feeling all right today.

13 ADA. Lovely, now I've done with that morning sickness. I believe some go on drooling for the full nine months, according to Trudy King.

14 MOONEY. Perhaps you ought to have a ground floor cell?

15 ADA. No thanks, ma'am . . . I'm used to my own little flowery. Is 'he' coming over?

16 MOONEY. The Governor . . . I'm expecting him any moment.

17 ADA. I wouldn't like him to see me like this. Ring if you need me, ma'am. I'll be off.

18 MOONEY. Very good, Ada.

Pause. A knock. The door opens.

1   GOVERNOR. Well, Miss Mooney!

2   MOONEY [*stands*]. Two hundred and eight. All correct, sir.

3   GOVERNOR. Thank you. Now what's this about this Ruth woman?

4   MOONEY. Sit here, sir. I'll pour you a cup of tea. Here's her file. She seems to be a headstrong girl.

5   GOVERNOR. Thanks. Bulky file for a girl of nineteen.

6   MOONEY. Biscuits?

7   GOVERNOR. Thanks. [*Drinking tea, munching biscuits. Reads.*] 'Absconded on four occasions', 'Ringleader of break-out from Moorland Detention School'. 'Threw missiles at Officers'. [*Alarmed.*] 'Flung heavy ink stand at Governor'. What a roll-up!

8   MOONEY. But have you noticed, sir, there are no 'bad' crimes in it.

9   GOVERNOR. Flung heavy ink stand at Governor. What do you call that?

10   MOONEY. She missed, sir.

11   GOVERNOR. What's she been up to this time?

12   MOONEY. She soaked Officer Stone.

13   GOVERNOR. How?

14   MOONEY. Here's the charge sheet, sir. Flung a bucket of water over her.

15   GOVERNOR. What's this about a mop?

16   MOONEY. She caught her with the mop, sir.

17   GOVERNOR. It says here she struck her with the mop. I'm sorry, Miss Mooney, I can't handle this. It's clear and simple assault. I'll have to send for a magistrate.

A slight pause.

18   MOONEY. Ah! Yes, maybe that would be the best thing, sir.

19   GOVERNOR. I can't sentence her—you know, I can only take away her good conduct remission.

1 MOONEY. I thought if we handled it quietly it might stop her from showing off. [*Imitating.*] 'They couldn't cope with me so they had to send for a magistrate'. I thought it might take her down a peg.

2 GOVERNOR [*abruptly*]. Right. I'll take it myself.

3 MOONEY. Very good, sir. I'll have Officer Preston arrange it.

Fade out.

Fade in the sharp marching footsteps of women. There is a knock on the door.

Sc. 7

4 MOONEY. Here they are, sir.

5 GOVERNOR. I'm ready.

6 MOONEY. Come in.

The door opens.

Ah, Officer Stone. Stand here will you?

7 STONE. Thank you.

8 MOONEY. Bring in the prisoner.

The door opens again.

9 PRESTON. Prisoner Lawrence! Bring her in.

10 JACKSON. In you go.

11 RUTH. Don't shove.

12 PRESTON. Stand on the mat, face the Governor, and declare your full name.

13 RUTH. Ruth Lawrence.

14 GOVERNOR. It has been reported, prisoner Lawrence, that at 2.30 p.m. today, whilst taking your admittance bath, supervised by Officer Stone, you picked up a long-handled mop and struck Officer Stone on the head. Further you plunged a bucket into the bath and flung the contents over the officer. Officer Stone, tell us what happened?

15 STONE. At the time and place stated, sir, I was in charge of the prisoner and others taking their bath. The prisoner

turned to me and said 'Scram to hell out of it, and let a body bath in peace.' I warned her that she would be reported. She said 'keep your eyes off me.' The next thing she picked up the mop and struck at me.

2 RUTH. I didn't strike. I only shoved it in your face.

3 MOONEY. Quiet! You may speak later. Yes ... Officer Stone?

4 STONE. Then the prisoner yelled to me: 'If you want your eye filling, this will fill it for you'. She grabbed a bucket and before I could get out of the way she had filled it in her bath and flung the hot soapy water over me. Officers Rigby and Platt came to my aid. The prisoner had got into her bath. But she was forcibly removed, and taken to her cell.

5 GOVERNOR. Thank you, Officer.

6 STONE. I had to make a complete change of clothes, sir.

7 GOVERNOR. I see. Now, Ruth Lawrence, what have you to say?

8 RUTH. I did shove the mop in her face, but I didn't strike her.

9 GOVERNOR. What's the difference?

10 RUTH. I only wanted to shove her out of the way. If I'd struck her it would have been because I wanted to hurt her. And she's not told the full tale.

11 GOVERNOR. What is your version?

12 RUTH. I had trouble with this officer at Reception. She began pushing me around over my dinner. When I got into my bath there was a morsel of carbolic soap. The size of a sixpence. I said to her 'Could I have some soap please?' She said to me 'Use the flaming scrubbing brush it's good enough for you.' The brush was worn down to the wood. And there I was trying to get a wash with a scrap of soap and a bit of board. And there was she grinning at me. So then I picked the mop up and shoved it in her face.

13 GOVERNOR. You admit then to assaulting an officer in the course of her duty.

1 RUTH. If you put it that way, sir. Another thing, I didn't like the way she looked. A bath is a private matter.

2 GOVERNOR. In prison there is nothing private.

3 RUTH. That's what you think.

4 PRESTON. Grab her!

5 STONE. I've got her.

Sounds of a struggle.

6 MOONEY. Let go. Prisoner Lawrence answer the Governor's questions.

7 GOVERNOR. Have you anything else to say? Very well. You will be confined to your cell for three days on number 2 diet. You will lose twenty-one days remission on your sentence. And I warn you, if you make any further trouble, we shall deal with you more severely. That will be all.

8 PRESTON. Come on.

Footsteps heard as the prisoner is marched off.

9 GOVERNOR. Officer Stone I'm very sorry this happened. I trust there will be no ill effects.

10 STONE. Thank you, sir.

11 GOVERNOR. Take the rest of the day off.

12 STONE. Thank you.

The door shuts.

13 MOONEY. A good looking lass, that Lawrence girl.

14 GOVERNOR. She'll make trouble. I could see by the way she held her head—and the look of defiance.

15 MOONEY. Is that what it was?

Fade out.

Fade in.

16 GOVERNOR. Any more applications this morning, Chief?

17 JENKINS. Just one more, sir—then Tillotson.

E

1 GOVERNOR. Right. Carry on.

2 JENKINS. Next.

3 BROWN. Very good, sir.

   Hatch door opening is heard.

   [*Shouts*]. Next applicant.

4 SMITH. Hy! Quick! In you go.

5 BROWN [*yells*]. Stand on the mat. Face the Governor. Declare your full name and number.

6 ADAMS [*with an American drawl*]. Pete Longfellow Adams. Number two, eight, three, one, two.

7 GOVERNOR. Yes, Adams?

8 ADAMS. Waal, sir, I'd like to ask your permission to write a letter to my old schoolmaster in California.

9 GOVERNOR. Why?

10 ADAMS. I wanna find out my real name. And I've gotta find out who my parents are.

11 GOVERNOR. Don't you know?

12 ADAMS. Not a ghost of any idea, sir. And I kind of figured it out that my old schoolmaster, a good man, might help me find out. And if he did, sir, I guess there'd be one problem less on m'mind. I don't like going round the world with the wrong name, and' not knowing rightly who my folks are.

13 GOVERNOR. Well, Chief Officer?

14 CHIEF. Prisoner abused previous petition. Wrote a pageful of obscene remarks about his mother.

15 GOVERNOR. I won't stand for that, Adams. However, you have one more chance to write the letter.

16 ADAMS. Thank you, sir.

17 BROWN. Off you go!

18 GOVERNOR [*to Chief*]. Is it true about his parents?

19 CHIEF [*casually*]. He doesn't know who they are, or what his name should be. But why he should write to

120

California I don't know—he was born in Thornaby-on-Tees, and never been out of the country.

2 GOVERNOR. I give up. Well . . . Tillotson now?

3 JENKINS. That's right, sir. Here's the tin of tobacco we found. Eight ounce.

4 GOVERNOR. Mermaid, pure gold Virginian leaf. Vacuum sealed. That's good stuff, chief. [*He opens the tin.*] Mmmm . . . smell . . .

5 JENKINS. Lovely! . . . wish I could afford that sort.

6 GOVERNOR. And where did you find it?

7 JENKINS. In a sack of cabbages, sir.

8 GOVERNOR. You're convinced that Tillotson was planning to pick it up?

9 JENKINS. I'm dead certain, sir. We got the tip-off about it. Young officer on duty, too eager, and he struck too soon. Tillotson hadn't picked the stuff up.

10 GOVERNOR. Bad timing.

11 JENKINS. He's so slippery, sir. For the last 18 months he's been the big baron here. Nearly all the smuggled-in tobacco goes through him. Now there's money in circulation. When we stripped the sole off of Makin's shoe yesterday, there was a fiver hidden away under it.

12 GOVERNOR. Have Tillotson brought in.

13 JENKINS [*yells*]. Fetch him in.

14 BROWN [*sotto voce*]. In with you, Tillotson. [*Shouts.*] Stand on the mat. Face the Governor. Declare your full name and number.

15 TILLOTSON. James Wheelwright Tillotson. Number five, eight, six, two, one.

16 GOVERNOR. Tillotson, what do you know about this tin of tobacco?

17 TILLOTSON. Nothing, sir. It smells lovely.

18 GOVERNOR. It was found in a sack of cabbages in the kitchen where you were working. Did you know it was there?

1 TILLOTSON. Me, sir! know it was there . . . ?

2 GOVERNOR. Come off it, Tillotson.

3 JENKINS. He was beside it. And it was planted there, sir, by whoever did it, for him to lift. Right amongst the cabbage leaves.

4 TILLOTSON. He's got no proof of that, sir.

5 GOVERNOR. I'm satisfied that you had planned to pick it up.

6 JENKINS. He certainly had, sir.

7 TILLOTSON. I deny it.

8 GOVERNOR. I didn't expect you to admit it. If you're caught trafficking it'll be another two years at least. You think we prison people are fools, and you consider yourself clever—but there's nothing clever in living out your manhood in a prison cell. Think over that, Tillotson. This time, we've no proof. There'll be no charge.

The telephone rings.

9 TILLOTSON. Thank you, sir.

10 JENKINS [*whispers*]. Off with you, Tillotson. We'll nab you the next time.

THE GOVERNOR *lifts the receiver.*

11 GOVERNOR. Hello. Governor. Yes, Miss Mooney. Prisoner Lawrence. What's she been up to now? She should still be on No. 2 diet. Eh? She is . . . but not eating it. You mean she's on hunger strike? Have you had the new M.O. to her? No? I'll see you about eleven o'clock. I'll bring the M.O. She must be fed.

Fade out.

Fade in.

12 MOONEY. Good morning to you. How do you feel?

13 RUTH. I'm all right.

1   MOONEY. You look pale. Now, about this not eating your food . . . The Governor and the Medical Officer have come to see you. Stand up, will you.

2   GOVERNOR. Young woman, are you refusing to eat?

3   RUTH. I'm just not hungry.

4   M.O. Let's take your pulse. When did she last eat, Miss Mooney?

5   MOONEY. Two days ago, when she was admitted.

6   GOVERNOR. That means you've never touched your punishment diet.

7   RUTH. Would you eat that filthy porridge?

8   GOVERNOR. I'd have no choice if I were in your position. It's an offence to refuse to eat, and if I were you I'd eat that plateful now and save us all a lot of trouble.

9   M.O. So you're determined not to? Well, you know what'll happen to you?

10   RUTH. Strap me down, stick the gag between my teeth and force the rubber tube down my throat.

11   M.O. She knows. Well, Miss Mooney, send her along to the Sick Bay.

12   GOVERNOR. Young woman, wouldn't you like to think it over? It's only a plateful of porridge.

13   RUTH. My mind's made up.

14   M.O. A waste of time.

15   GOVERNOR. I'm afraid you're right. Miss Mooney, have the prisoner sent to the Sick Bay.

16   MOONEY. Very good, sir.

The door clangs shut.

Just a moment. I'd like to go back and have a word with her.

17   GOVERNOR. It's no use.

18   M.O. You can do nothing with her sort. I've handled too many of them.

1 MOONEY. I'll not be a minute. Officer, unlock the cell again.

Sound of cell door being unlocked.

2 RUTH. You back again?

3 MOONEY [*cheerful sigh*]. Do you mind if I sit down there beside you?

4 RUTH. No.

5 MOONEY. Oh, my poor feet. Walking about this prison all day long. [*Cheerful groan.*]

6 RUTH. If you've come back to try and get me to eat that stuff you're wasting your time.

7 MOONEY. Don't you start telling me! That's what those two have been saying outside. [*Sits down with a groan.*] It must be grand to be young. Are you from the town or the country?

8 RUTH [*eager*]. Country!

9 MOONEY. I thought you were. You have that fresh skin. Father and Mother still there?

10 RUTH [*angry*]. I have no father or mother!

11 MOONEY. Sorry. I didn't know they were dead.

12 RUTH. They're dead to me.

13 MOONEY. That's a hard thing to say. [*Detached.*] I never knew mine. I was brought up in an orphanage. But to this day I feel an empty place in me.

Pause.

14 RUTH. Sorry.

15 MOONEY. Seems it all turns out for the best. This cell must be nice and cool on a hot day.

16 RUTH. That's about all you could say for it.

Pause.

17 MOONEY. Would you like a taste of this chocolate?

1 RUTH. No, thank you.

2 MOONEY. Look, I don't care whether you eat the porridge or not. And if I could see some place here to fling it away without it being known, I'd do that. And I'll tell you another thing—if I was in your place I wouldn't eat it either.

3 RUTH. Do you mean that?

4 MOONEY. Of course I do. Cold porridge—pooh! Here . . . have a taste of chocolate.

5 RUTH. Thanks.

6 MOONEY. Watch they don't see us through that Judas spy-hole. I wouldn't want them to feed *me* by a tube. A woman can be determined—but she needs to keep her dignity.

7 RUTH. A fat chance you've got in prison.

8 MOONEY. I won't beat about the bush. I did come back here to try to talk you round.

9 RUTH [*sharp*]. You haven't an earthly.

10 MOONEY. I know that. Listen, if I eat half of the porridge, will you eat the other half?

11 RUTH. Are you mad?

12 MOONEY. I'm not sure. But I have to keep my side of the prison in order. I know I can't spare the officers that will have to attend you in and out of the Sick Bay. I can't stand a lot of fuss.

13 RUTH. You'd never eat that muck.

14 MOONEY. Just watch.

Sound of plate and spoon and eating.

[*Mouth full*]. Who said I wouldn't?

15 RUTH [*starts laughing*]. It's all down your chin.

16 MOONEY. And now . . . here's your half . . .

1   RUTH [*cheerfully*]. All right. You win . . .

    Fade out on the sounds of eating.

Fade in on the choir singing with great spirit. A woman's solo part sung by RUTH *brings the singing to an end.*

2   GOVERNOR. Good. We're coming along nicely. Now let's turn back to the overture.

    Shuffling of music.

3   DAVIS [*prison whisper*]. Tillotson, who's the new soprano?

4   TILLOTSON [*whispers*]. A kid called Ruth Lawrence.

5   DAVIS. Ain't she got a cracking voice!

6   TILLOTSON. She looks all right as well. She's lovely.

7   DAVIS. How do you know?

8   TILLOTSON. See that top corner window of the chapel. When the sun shines in the right spot you get a glimpse of her reflection. Look! Up there now. That's her! . . .

9   DAVIS [*low whistle of surprise*]. Coo! Mind your 'ead, let me see her. Nice bit of stuff.

10   TILLOTSON. I'm sending her this note . . . over the screen. 'Dear Ruth, Since you came to sing in the choir, it has made all the difference to my life. You are like a lark amongst a bunch of crows. Your voice does something to me. Sometimes I can see your face in the top left-hand chapel window. I think you are a lovely girl. All night long in my cell I see your face. Look for me one day. I hope we can meet when I go out. Love, T.'

11   DAVIS. You can't send that! . . . not with your initial at the bottom. If a screw catches it, they'll know it's you . . .

12   TILLOTSON. I'll risk it. As soon as the choir starts singing, I'll make it up into a little pellet. Over the top it'll go and ping clean down on her music sheet.

1 GOVERNOR. Quiet. Ready?

The organ starts and the choir begins to sing. Ruth's voice leads as we fade out.

Fade in on footsteps along the prison corridor.

2 STONE. Back into your cells.

Clanging of cell doors.

3 RUTH. Now I must read my little love letter. [*Reads.*] 'Dear Ruth, Since you came to sing in the choir, it has made all the difference to my life. You are like a lark amongst a bunch of crows. [*Laughs.*] Your voice does something to me. Sometimes when I see your face . . .'

Fade out.

Fade in.

4 MOONEY. Well, Ada, are you all ready?

5 ADA. I think so. I've got my little bag here with all my things in.

6 MOONEY. The car calls for you at two o'clock. You will be driven straight to the Maternity Home. It's called 'The Larches', and it's in Queen's Crescent.

7 ADA. That will be a nice address on his birth certificate!

8 MOONEY. It's really for the baby's sake you're going out. Now no-one will know you come from here unless you tell them.

9 ADA. I'm not going to advertise that fact.

10 MOONEY. Good. The Governor has given your home address.

11 ADA. He thinks of everything, doesn't he, ma'am.

12 MOONEY. Your confinement will be in two days' time, according to the doctor, but we're taking no chances. We mustn't have him born in prison.

1 ADA. There could be worse places.

2 MOONEY. Yes, but he might not think so in days to come. You will stay there ten days, then you'll come back. Baby will stay with you in your cell for the first few months. We've got a nice little cot. Then he'll go in the crèche.

3 ADA. Then I'll be going out when he is seven months old. I don't know how to thank you, ma'am.

4 MOONEY. Well, I hope we don't have to do it again for you, Ada.

5 ADA. No, not with Baby. I won't come in again.

6 MOONEY. You must be a bit of a home bird, Ada, be more ambitious for your home.

7 ADA. It was ambition got me inside again ma'am. I went in for all cut-glass and hall-marked silver. I'll be satisfied with Woolworths next time . . . Something I must show you. Look at this lovely little baby coat.

8 MOONEY. That *is* lovely.

9 ADA. Who do you think knitted it? Ruth Lawrence. She's wonderful with her fingers. He'd have been going to school before *I'd* have finished it. I'll miss her, you know

10 MOONEY. She seems to be settling down, Ada.

11 ADA. Ruth's a lovely little girl, if they'll only leave her alone. She gets on well with all of us. But I often expect when Officer Stone goes near her that there's going to be a bust-up again. You can see her, the way the fire comes into her eyes. You, ma'am, seem to be the only one that can manage her. She likes you.

12 MOONEY. I'm glad to hear it.

Footsteps approaching.

13 ADA. Oh, here's the Governor, ma'am. I don't want him to see me like this. I'll go and do a bit in the kitchen.

The door opens.

14 GOVERNOR. Good morning, Ada.

1 ADA. Good morning, excuse me, will you, sir. [*Hastily.*]

2 GOVERNOR. Morning, Miss Mooney.

3 MOONEY. Two hundred and fourteen. All correct, sir. Good morning.

4 GOVERNOR. Ada seems a bit bashful today.

5 MOONEY. She's going off to have her baby. Ruth knitted her a lovely wee jacket for her baby.

6 GOVERNOR. How nice. I must say Ruth has made a difference to the choir. When does she go out?

7 MOONEY. Six weeks' time.

8 GOVERNOR. I'm going to miss her. By the way, what about those people you wrote to about her?

9 MOONEY. I've got the correspondence here. This is a letter from the headmistress of her local school. [*Reads.*] 'I cannot tell you how terribly upset we have all been by what happened to Ruth. It came as the greatest shock to us all. She came to my school as a child of five, and for eleven years was one of our best pupils. She was eager and impetuous, and would respond at once to encouragement, but was touchy about criticism. Her high-spirited enthusiasm carried others along with her. And she was a very popular school captain.'

10 GOVERNOR. I can well imagine that.

11 MOONEY. 'When she left us to go to Hillbury County School, where she was to be a weekly boarder, we had the greatest confidence in her ability to fit herself in to her new surroundings, and to work well there. She was a girl of singular determination. But she was essentially a happy girl. I can only believe that some grievous hurt so changed her. It has been painful to write this testimony. Yours sincerely, Elizabeth Appleyard.'

12 GOVERNOR. What about Hillbury County School?

13 MOONEY. As soon as she arrived she began to steal. [*Reads.*] 'A number of articles had disappeared, amongst which were three fountain pens, a ring, a watch, a book of poems, and some chocolate. Ruth Lawrence was

suspected and sent for. She refused to open her locker, and I told her we should have to open it by force. She flew into a rage and it took four mistresses and a school porter to overcome her.'

2 GOVERNOR. She must have been tough even in those days.

3 MOONEY [*continues reading*]. Her locker was opened in her presence and after an outburst of shocking language, she collapsed. The articles were all found intact, except the ring, a gold one, which she had apparently attempted to stamp out of shape. The chocolate was untouched. Even then, I decided against expelling her. I had noticed at times that she could be a singularly pleasant pupil, and she was certainly quite brilliant. However, she took the matter out of my hands by running away that very night. I reported it at once to her parents and the police. She did not return home and I understand it was five weeks before she was found. Please treat this letter as confidential. Yours faithfully, Alicia Spengle.'

4 GOVERNOR. I wonder what happened to her between leaving her first school and going to the second?

5 MOONEY. I only wish we knew. Something sent her off the rails.

6 GOVERNOR. Where does she go when she goes out of prison?

7 MOONEY. That's the worry. She won't go home. She just goes off, then she gets into trouble.

8 GOVERNOR. What about her parents?

9 MOONEY. They'd love to see her, but she won't see them. They seem very decent respectable people. He's a gardener.

10 GOVERNOR. I think we should have a chat with them. It might help to clear matters up. Try it for a week Saturday. It can do no harm.

11 MOONEY. Very well, sir. I'll send them rail tickets.

1   GOVERNOR. It would be cheaper for the country than having her in again, if we do something about it now. Pity if a kid like that becomes an old lag.

Fade out.

Fade in.

2   PRESTON. Mr. and Mrs. Lawrence are here.

3   MOONEY. Show them in at once and let the Governor know.

4   PRESTON. Come this way, please.

The door opens.

5   MOONEY. Come in. Mrs. Lawrence I'm very pleased to meet you. I'm Miss Mooney.

6   MRS. LAWRENCE. Pleased to meet you, Miss Mooney.

7   MOONEY. Mr. Lawrence, how nice of you to come.

8   MR. LAWRENCE. Pleased to meet you, Miss Mooney. It was very good of you to send us the tickets. Mother . . .

9   MRS. LAWRENCE. Yes, you must let us pay you back, Miss Mooney.

10   MOONEY. Not at all.

11   MR. LAWRENCE. But we insist. It's not the money that's kept us from visiting her, you know.

12   MOONEY. Oh, I know that. The service sends tickets when it seems it would be a good thing for us to meet a girl's parents. Do sit down. Ah, here's the Governor now.

The door opens.

13   GOVERNOR. Good afternoon.

14   MOONEY. Two hundred and sixteen. All correct, sir. Here's Mr. and Mrs. Lawrence. This is Mr. Keen, the Governor.

15   GOVERNOR. How do you do, Mrs. Lawrence.

1   MRS. LAWRENCE. Pleased to meet you, sir.

2   GOVERNOR. How do you do, Mr. Lawrence.

3   MR. LAWRENCE. I'm quite well, thank you, and pleased to meet you.

4   GOVERNOR. You must be tired after your journey.

5   MR. LAWRENCE. We're not used to travelling. Mother did have a bit of a headache, but I think it's gone now.

6   MRS. LAWRENCE. I feel all right now, Dad.

7   MOONEY. Tea'll be here any moment.

8   MRS. LAWRENCE. I wouldn't say no to a cup of tea.

9   MOONEY. Do you know, that Ruth's sentence will be over in a few weeks, and she'll be going out.

10   MR. LAWRENCE. No, we didn't know. She never writes to us. All we hear is from the Police Court.

11   MOONEY. Will she be going back home to you?

12   MRS. LAWRENCE. No! I wish she were! We haven't had her at home since she was sixteen.

13   MR. LAWRENCE [*low and eager*]. How is our Ruth?

14   MOONEY. Oh, she's very well. Never seen her in better spirits.

15   MRS. LAWRENCE [*whisper*]. How's she been behaving?

16   MOONEY. Oh, quite well of late.

17   GOVERNOR. She's a head-strong girl and she has a temper. Often makes things hard for herself, and for our officers.

18   MRS. LAWRENCE. Aye, she always had a temper, didn't she, Dad?

19   MR. LAWRENCE. I wouldn't say that. She wouldn't be put off anything she'd set her mind on. But she was never bad tempered.

The door opens.

20   MOONEY. Here's the tea. Sugar, Mrs. Lawrence?

1 MRS. LAWRENCE. Yes, please. Thank you.

2 MOONEY. Mr. Lawrence?

3 MR. LAWRENCE. If you please, ma'am. Thank you.

Sound of cups and saucers.

4 GOVERNOR. May I pass the sandwiches round, Miss Mooney?

5 MOONEY. Please do. Perhaps Mr. and Mrs. Lawrence would have liked a proper meal?

6 MRS. LAWRENCE. Tea's just what I want.

7 MR. LAWRENCE. Nothing heavy for me, thank you.

The eating and drinking continues under the dialogue.

8 GOVERNOR. Ruth . . . she's your only child?

9 MR. LAWRENCE. Yes.

10 MRS. LAWRENCE. We've no other.

11 GOVERNOR. Was she difficult in other ways?

12 MR. LAWRENCE. She wasn't difficult in no way, sir. She was proud—not difficult.

13 GOVERNOR. Had she any special interests—hobbies?

14 MRS. LAWRENCE. She was very fond of the country. She knew the names of all the little flowers you get along the hedgerows.

15 MR. LAWRENCE. Birds, too. I'll bet she could name nearly every bird in the British Isles . . . at least in our part of it.

16 MOONEY. It must be very hard for her now . . . away from it all.

17 MR. LAWRENCE. Many's the night I've thought of her, locked away in a prison cell and she so fond of the sky and stars and the fresh air.

18 MOONEY. You've no idea what happened to her?

19 MRS. LAWRENCE. It has been a mystery to us.

20 MR. LAWRENCE. There was . . .

1 MRS. LAWRENCE [*interrupts*]. I wish we'd never let her go to that school.

2 MR. LAWRENCE. It seems she never fitted in there. That day we saw her at the Police Station, after she'd been wandering about for five weeks, you never saw such a change in a girl.

3 MRS. LAWRENCE. She was like a wild thing, wasn't she, Dad? And she wouldn't speak to us ... made out she didn't even know us.

4 GOVERNOR. Well, she looks very well now. Would you like to see her?

5 MR. LAWRENCE. Oh, we'd love to!

6 MRS. LAWRENCE. Oh, yes! But we wouldn't like to upset her. You know she's always refused to see us, wherever we've gone to visit her.

7 MOONEY. You've no idea why Ruth won't see you?

8 MR. LAWRENCE. No ma'am except ...

9 MRS. LAWRENCE. No, we'd no idea. I only wish we'd never let her go to that school.

10 MR. LAWRENCE. We rue the day that happened.

11 MOONEY. What were you going to say, Mr. Lawrence?

12 MR. LAWRENCE. Well, it was nothing in a way, and yet I've always felt that was at the bottom of it.

13 MRS. LAWRENCE. It couldn't have been, Dad.

14 GOVERNOR. What was that?

15 MR. LAWRENCE. We had to tell her something, the night before she went away.

16 MRS. LAWRENCE. Yes, just in case someone else told her.

17 MOONEY. What was it you had to tell her?

18 MRS. LAWRENCE. Dad, you tell.

19 MR. LAWRENCE. We had to tell her she wasn't our daughter.

20 MOONEY. She's not really your daughter?

21 MR. LAWRENCE. I'm afraid she isn't.

22 GOVERNOR. She didn't know—?

1   MR. LAWRENCE. She'd no idea.

2   MOONEY. It must have come as a shock.

3   MR. LAWRENCE. I'd have given everything to draw back my words once I'd spoken.

4   MRS. LAWRENCE. We had to tell her, Dad. It was better we told her than someone else.

5   GOVERNOR. What happened when you told her?

6   MRS. LAWRENCE. She didn't want to believe—she didn't want to hear.

7   MOONEY. How did you come to tell her?

8   MR. LAWRENCE. She needed her birth certificate.

9   MRS. LAWRENCE. That was the night before she had to leave for her new school the next morning.

10 MR. LAWRENCE. Of course we should have told her sooner.

11 MRS. LAWRENCE. But we never had need to, Dad.

12 MR. LAWRENCE. We had her from birth, you know, sir, she was born under our roof.

13 MRS. LAWRENCE. Her mother, poor girl, was in service at my old place. A Welsh girl, and a pretty thing she was too. It was a soldier stationed at Taunton that got her into trouble. He was sent on a draft to India and that was the last she ever saw of him.

14 MR. LAWRENCE. We took the little girl in, and she had the baby under our roof. She kept the whole thing secret from her own parents.

15 GOVERNOR. Did you adopt Ruth legally?

16 MRS. LAWRENCE. We didn't go to solicitors or sign papers, sir . . . we weren't out to rob young Helen of her child.

17 MR. LAWRENCE. We hadn't decided on adoption at the time. We'd kind of got used to the idea of having no family of our own. But I didn't know how a child grows on you. A month later when the mother went back to Wales we said we'd keep Ruth for life. And we were happy at the prospect.

1 MRS. LAWRENCE. We never saw Helen again, and we got that we looked on Ruth as our own flesh and blood.

2 MR. LAWRENCE. She came into our home like a gift from God.

3 MOONEY. What happened when you told her?

4 MR. LAWRENCE. She wouldn't believe us.

5 MRS. LAWRENCE. When I saw how strange her face was, I gave Dad a look and we dropped the matter. Dad said: 'I'll never broach it again the longest day I live'.

6 MR. LAWRENCE. But that night we could hear her walking about her room, so I went into her to comfort her.

7 MRS. LAWRENCE. Dad could always talk her round.

8 MR. LAWRENCE. But not that time I couldn't. She started screaming at me, then Mother came in. I don't want you two—she cried at us. I want my own mother and father.

9 MRS. LAWRENCE. I've nobody now, she said, no cousins, no uncles or aunts. I've no real relatives . . . I'm all alone. But you're not, I said. We're just the same. We're your mother and father. You're not, she said. You've lied to me. It was no use talking to her. That was the last night she spent under our roof.

10 MOONEY. I am very sorry for you both. It must have been very hard.

11 GOVERNOR. Look here, why not have Ruth come along now and meet you?

12 MRS. LAWRENCE. She'd never come if she knew we were here.

13 MR. LAWRENCE. She has always refused to see us. Something got into her that night, and nothing can move it.

14 GOVERNOR. Then we won't tell her who wants to see her, let it come as a surprise.

15 MOONEY. That would be very risky, sir.

16 GOVERNOR. She's improved so much lately, it's a risk worth while taking. What do you think, Mr. Lawrence?

136

1   MR. LAWRENCE. I don't rightly know.

2   GOVERNOR. And you, Mrs. Lawrence.

3   MRS. LAWRENCE. I wouldn't like to upset her, but it is years since we were together—and perhaps if we could get talking about home she might be all right. She was a girl that was liked by everybody. They missed her, and she must have missed them.

4   MR. LAWRENCE. But I wouldn't like to spring it on her, Mother.

5   MOONEY. I'm afraid I wouldn't like to take the risk.

6   GOVERNOR. I think it'll be all right, Miss Mooney, let's try it. Have her sent for.

7   MOONEY. If you insist, sir.

She lifts the telephone.

8   MOONEY. Miss Preston, bring Ruth Lawrence to my office, will you? Just tell her I want to see her, nothing more. Thank you.

She replaces the receiver.

Ruth will be here in two or three minutes.

9   GOVERNOR. Would you like us to leave you alone?

10   MRS. LAWRENCE. I'd rather you stay, for the first minute or so.

11   MR. LAWRENCE. Aye, it might be as well.

There is a pause. Some fidgeting can be heard and then a knock on the door. The door opens.

12   PRESTON. Prisoner Lawrence is here, ma'am.

13   MOONEY. Show her in, please.

14   PRESTON. Prisoner Lawrence, go right in.

15   RUTH. Miss Mooney, you wanted me . . . Oh, and you, sir.

16   MOONEY. Yes, Ruth. Someone here to see you.

17   RUTH. See me . . . [*She stops suddenly.*]

18   MR. LAWRENCE [*after a pause*]. It's us, Ruth.

1   MRS. LAWRENCE. We wanted so much to see you.

2   RUTH. I don't want to see you. I don't even know you.

3   GOVERNOR. Ruth, your Mother and Father.

4   RUTH. I have no mother and father. I know who'd done this trick on me. Miss Mooney, you have. And I trusted you. But you're as bad as the rest of them.

Sounds of a scuffle.

5   PRESTON. Ruth, keep still.

6   MR. LAWRENCE. Ruthy! Ruthy dear.

7   GOVERNOR. Ruth!

8   PRESTON. I've got her, sir. Ruth get off my toe.

9   MOONEY. Miss Preston, please let go of her.

10   PRESTON. Is it safe, ma'am?

11   MOONEY. Let go please. Ruth, I'm terribly sorry.

12   RUTH. Sir, I want to go back to my cell.

13   GOVERNOR. Miss Preston, please escort the prisoner back to her cell.

14   MRS. LAWRENCE. Ruth! . . . Ruth.

The door closes.

15   MR. LAWRENCE. Now then, Edith . . .

16   MRS. LAWRENCE. Our poor little Ruth . . . [*She sobs.*]

17   MOONEY. I'm terribly sorry . . .

18   GOVERNOR. I'm afraid I blundered there.

19   MR. LAWRENCE. You both did your best, sir. She's our daughter . . . but the Lord knows we didn't bring her up that way.

20   MRS. LAWRENCE. I'd like to go home, Dad.

21   GOVERNOR. I'll run you to the station.

22   MRS. LAWRENCE. They won't be too harsh on her, sir . . . back in her cell.

23   GOVERNOR. No . . . nothing will happen to her. The officers aren't so severe when I'm not there.

1 MR. LAWRENCE. Don't take it so badly, Miss Mooney. For a second there I saw the old Ruth look . . . I thought she was going to run into my arms.

2 MRS. LAWRENCE. So did I!

3 MR. LAWRENCE. She was such a gentle maid . . . it's hard to think what came over her.

4 MOONEY. We mustn't give up hope. Well, goodbye Mrs. Lawrence. Goodbye, Mr. Lawrence.

5 GOVERNOR. I'll get the car.

6 MRS. LAWRENCE. You'll look after our little girl for us, Miss Mooney?

7 MOONEY. I will. I promise you that.

8 MR. LAWRENCE. Thank you, ma'am. Goodbye.

Fade out.

Fade in.

9 PRESTON. Miss Mooney, it's turned six, are you going off now?

10 MOONEY. I'm waiting for Mr. Keen. How was she when you got her back to her cell?

11 PRESTON. She flung herself down on her bed.

12 MOONEY. Did she cry?

13 PRESTON. Oh no . . . I've never seen Ruth cry.

14 MOONEY. It might be a good thing if she did.

15 PRESTON. She'll need to soften up a lot before she does.

Faint sounds of breaking glass and yells can be heard in the distance.

16 PRESTON. Did you hear that?

17 MOONEY. Somebody letting off steam . . .

The cries are now louder and can be heard to be RUTH'S. Fierce knocking on door. The door opens.

1 STONE [*out of breath*]. Lawrence is smashing up her cell.

2 MOONEY [*calm*]. Have any officers gone in to her?

3 STONE. No, ma'am, not yet. She has a chair leg in her hand. She looks violent.

4 MOONEY. What happened?

5 STONE. I lifted up the cover of the observation hole and I saw her slip off her shoe and crash her heel through the small panes of glass as quick as she could. Then she grabbed her chair and smashed it and held up a chair leg and dared any of us to enter.

6 PRESTON. We'd better go in to her, hadn't we?

There is a tap on the door.

7 GOVERNOR. Hello, what's going on now?

8 MOONEY. 216 all correct, sir. Prisoner Lawrence smashing up her cell.

9 GOVERNOR. Well, why hasn't she been stopped?

10 STONE. She's very violent, sir.

11 MOONEY. Miss Stone, Miss Preston, you'd better go off and keep the others quiet.

12 PRESTON. Very good.

13 STONE. Suppose the prisoner injures herself?

14 MOONEY. I don't think she will. Just keep calm.

15 GOVERNOR. You expected this?

16 MOONEY. I expected something.

17 GOVERNOR. Why didn't you have her stopped at once?

18 MOONEY. I didn't get the chance, and once she'd done the damage, it was better to let her get it all out of her system. And I didn't want any of my officers hurt.

There are sounds of uproar and women yelling.

19 GOVERNOR. Now she's set them all off!

20 MOONEY [*calm*]. It's harmless enough—a bit of yelling and shouting does 'em good. It's the weekend. And besides, they're all safe in their cells.

1 GOVERNOR. But it must be stopped.

2 MOONEY. Yes, sir. We'll go along to Ruth's cell.

Fade out.

Fade in on the sound of crashing and smashing in a cell.

3 RUTH [*temper with bursts of joy*]. Yah, you bunch of lousy screws . . . Why don't you come in and get me? Scared . . . ? [*Kicks and sound of furniture thrown.*] That's what I think of your rotten prison furniture. [*Tearing sound.*] That's put paid to your mattress. Don't spy on me . . . get away from that Judas hole.

A loud crash.

4 STONE. Ooh! That nearly came through the door.

5 GREENHALSH. Here, let me have a look at her. Crikey! I wish I had her energy.

6 PRESTON. Here's the Governor and Miss Mooney! Out of the way.

7 GOVERNOR. She's still at it?

8 PRESTON. Just tearing up her mattress, sir.

9 RUTH [*yells*]. I dare you . . . any one of you . . . to open that cell door. And I'll let you have it with this . . .

10 PRESTON. Sir, she's got a nasty chunk of glass in her hand.

11 GOVERNOR. Let me have a look. Mmm, that looks dangerous.

12 STONE. If we had the hose, sir, we could give her a soaking, and then rush in and put the straight-jacket on her.

13 GOVERNOR. Here's Miss Mooney. We'll see what she has to say.

14 MOONEY. How is she now, sir?

15 GOVERNOR. She's got a chunk of glass. Just you have a look.

16 MOONEY. That looks ugly.

17 RUTH. Come in and get me. Why don't you? What are you waiting for you rotten bunch of cowards?

1 GOVERNOR. Well, Miss Mooney, have you any suggestion before we turn the hose on her?

2 MOONEY. I think if you spoke to her, sir, you'd calm her down.

3 GOVERNOR. Spoke to her? She can't hear me unless I yell my head off.

4 MOONEY. I mean, go in to her, sir. Speak to her inside. I don't think she'd throw that glass at you.

5 GOVERNOR. Let's hope you're right. Well, something's got to be done. Miss Preston, get ready to unlock the door. One of you go below and have one of the . . . padded cells ready for her. You others stand back in case she does throw it. Ready, Miss Preston?

6 PRESTON. Yes, sir. I'll unlock it.

She turns the key in the lock.

7 GOVERNOR. Stand back.

8 RUTH. I'll let you have it, the first who puts a foot in my cell.

9 GOVERNOR. This is the Governor speaking. I'm coming in to you.

He flings the door open. There is a dead silence.

Ruth Lawrence, put that piece of glass down.

10 RUTH. What . . . ?

11 GOVERNOR. Put it down.

Pause. She drops the glass on the floor.

Ruth, I don't want to use force. I want you to promise you'll come along quietly with me.

12 RUTH. Yes, sir. I'll come with you. Excuse me a minute, while I tidy my hair and dress. That's better. Mind your feet on the broken glass.

13 GOVERNOR. Here, take my arm.

1   RUTH. Thank you, sir.

Footsteps are heard evenly along corridor.

2   PRESTON. Going off like a bridal pair. Who would have thought it!

3   MOONEY. Better than using a hosepipe.

Fade out.

Fade in on gentle knocking on door.

4   MOONEY. Come in.

5   ADA. It's only me, ma'am.

6   MOONEY. Ada! You're back again!

7   ADA. And I've got little Jeremy with me.

8   MOONEY. Oh, let me look at him. What a lovely little boy God bless him.

9   ADA. Eight-and-a-half pounds at birth.

10 MOONEY. The diet here isn't as bad as some people make out, Ada. It'll be nice to have a baby in again.

11 ADA. I hope the women don't spoil him.

12 MOONEY. It'll be a change to have somebody spoilt in prison. How was the nursing home?

13 ADA. Well . . . it's always nice to be back amongst your own again. That's the little jacket Ruth knitted him. Doesn't it look nice?

14 MOONEY. Very nice indeed.

15 ADA [*whispers*]. I heard she had a smash-up, ma'am.

16 MOONEY. Yes.

17 ADA. And the Governor's put her in the padded cell.

18 MOONEY. Well, we didn't want to have another, you know.

19 ADA. She's no more mad than I am, ma'am. Every woman feels like flying off the handle now and again. I'll bet there's times when you could charge round your office and smash everything up to smithereens.

1 MOONEY. I'm past it now . . .

2 ADA. It's a shame to have Ruth in one of those cells for a single night. Everything stuck to the floor and that horrible yellow light on night and day.

3 MOONEY. The Governor will let her out the moment she gives her word to behave.

Fade out.

Fade in on pacing footsteps on a rubber floor.

4 RUTH [*very sane*]. I'll go mad if I'm kept in here another five minutes. I'm sick of the sight of rubber. Rubber chair, rubber seats.

The door opens.

5 PRESTON. Your lunch.

6 RUTH. I can't eat with that spoon.

7 PRESTON. Sorry, nothing I can do about it.

8 RUTH. How much longer is he keeping me in here?

9 PRESTON. Until you behave. You can't go smashing up cells and get away with it. If you hadn't been put in here, he'd have had to have brought a magistrate along and you'd have got an extra three months on your sentence. You can't have it both ways.

10 RUTH. I'd do twelve months, before another night in here.

11 PRESTON. All you've got to do is tell him. You'll get let out then.

12 RUTH. Why should I make a promise to him? I'm just in here to serve my time and then go out.

13 PRESTON. Come to your senses, girl. He'll be down in five minutes. I'm off.

She closes the door. Ruth hums a melancholy tune. The door opens again.

14 PRESTON. Governor to see you.

15 GOVERNOR. Well, how are you today?

1   RUTH. When are you letting me out of this place?

2   GOVERNOR. As soon as you'll give me your word to behave.

3   RUTH. I hate that light glaring down on me all night. Can I
      have it out?

4   GOVERNOR. Sorry. We must be able to see you night and
      day. Are you going to give me your word?

5   RUTH. Why should I? Mooney played a dirty trick on me.

6   GOVERNOR. You mean Miss Mooney? She didn't send for
      you when your parents were here.

7   RUTH. She didn't . . . ?

8   GOVERNOR. No, I did. The Medical Officer will come and
      look at you later. Good-day. Unlock the door, Miss
      Preston.

9   RUTH. Stop!

10 PRESTON. Just a moment, sir! The prisoner wishes to speak
      to you.

11 RUTH. I give you my word.

12 GOVERNOR. Very good. Miss Preston, Prisoner Lawrence is to
      go back to her own cell and be issued with her own
      uniform.

13 PRESTON. Very good, sir.

14 GOVERNOR. Thank you, Miss Preston. Good-day.

15 PRESTON. Good-day, sir. Ready, Ruth?

16 RUTH. I'm ready.

17 PRESTON. You know what you need?

18 RUTH. What?

19 PRESTON. A jolly good hiding. It would do you a world of
      good.

20 RUTH [*cheerfully*]. You could be right at that.

      Fade out.

_____

Fade in on the choir singing badly. Suddenly the singing is halted in the middle.

21 GOVERNOR. Stop! Enough! What's up with you all today?

145

There is a silence.

Never heard worse singing in my life!

2 TILLOTSON. Sir, we're missing our soprano.

3 GOVERNOR. Sopranos are like tenors, they come and go.

4 DAVIS [*prison whisper*]. Tillotson, she's not gone out, has she?

5 TILLOTSON. No. She smashed up her flowery. He's had her in the padded cell.

6 DAVIS. Then she'll be back singing on Saturday.

7 TILLOTSON. Saturday? . . . We'll not be here then.

8 DAVIS. Turn it in, Tilly, case anybody hears you.

9 GOVERNOR. Silence. I think we'd better end our choir practice for today. I hope you're in better voice next time. [*Calls to officers who stand outside Chapel door.*] Officer Brown!

10 BROWN. Yes, sir.

11 GOVERNOR. Come in and take your party. Officer Greenhalsh!

12 GREENHALSH. Yes, sir.

13 GOVERNOR. Your party.

14 BROWN [*counts*]. Line up there! [*Mutters.*] . . . Two, four, six, eight, ten, twelve. [*Calls.*] Twelve. All correct, sir.

15 GOVERNOR. Very good, Officer.

16 GREENHALSH [*mutters*]. One, two, three, four, five . . . eleven. [*Calls.*] All correct, sir. Eleven.

17 BROWN. Right, back to your cells.

18 GOVERNOR. Thank you, Officer.

Sound of feet marching off.

19 JENKINS. Sir . . .

20 GOVERNOR. Yes, Chief Officer?

21 JENKINS. Telephone message. Your deputy Captain Schofield, sir. Sent word from the hospital that he would be back on duty next Monday.

22 GOVERNOR. Good. Anything on your mind, Chief?

1 JENKINS. There's a funny mood about the place I don't like. Quiet, like something was brewing.

2 GOVERNOR. Have you been tipped off?

3 JENKINS. Nothing definite, sir. When I passed Tillotson there, he'd a funny little smirk on his face.

4 GOVERNOR. Let's keep calm, and keep our eyes open.

5 JENKINS. That's what I'm doing, sir.

Fade out.

Fade in a clock striking eight. There is a knocking on the door.

6 GOVERNOR. Come in.

7 JENKINS. You're working late, sir.

8 GOVERNOR. I'll be leaving in a minute.

9 JENKINS. I'm just making my last round, sir.

The telephone rings. The GOVERNOR *lifts the receiver.*

10 GOVERNOR. Governor speaking. What's that? Bar removed from skylight in the tailoring shop? Have you checked up? Who'd been working there? Tillotson, Davis, Brooks. Get through, see if are they on the roof. Keep watch up there, but be careful. We'll check their cells.

He replaces the receiver.

11 JENKINS. What's that, sir?

12 GOVERNOR. Skylight in the tailor's shop. Call immediate check up of every prisoner. Put security guard on gate. Call emergency squad at first notice.

13 JENKINS. I'll check on D. Block at once, sir, for Tillotson.

He lifts the receiver.

Chief Officer here. Get me D. block at once. Alert the gate too. There might be something doing. Ring Officers' Club at once. Get every man in D. Block?

Is that you Fowler? Check on Tillotson and Davis'.
cells at once. Hurry. [*Pause.*] Well, sir, we'll soon knows
Fowler . . . [*Shouts.*] What! Right. Make a complete
check of the block . . .

He replaces the receiver.

Tillotson and Davis and Brooks cells are empty, sir.

2 GOVERNOR. Must sound the alarm.

The alarm bell sounds.

3 JENKINS. That'll fetch 'em in, sir.

4 GOVERNOR. You take some men up to the roof of the
tailor's shop.

5 JENKINS. Very good, sir. But if they're stuck up there they
can't escape. It's a good distance from there to the
top of the prison wall.

6 GOVERNOR. They might have rigged up a ladder.

7 JENKINS. Yes, sir.

8 GOVERNOR. I'll meet the emergency men at the gate.

Door slams. The prison bell rings louder.

Governor here. Lenegan, you're on the Gate tonight?

9 LENEGAN. Yes, sir. Here's the squad now.

Men's running footsteps can be heard across the yard.

10 PRISON OFFICERS. Lenegan, who's out now?
Anybody away?
I know that if ever I am winning a game of snooker,
the alarm would go off.

11 LENEGAN. The governor's waiting for you.

12 GOVERNOR. Right everybody. Tillotson, Davis and Brooks
are out of their cells. There might be others, you three,
Bates, Freeman and Elliott.

13 VOICES. Yes, sir.

14 GOVERNOR. Patrol round the prison walls. Keep special
watch opposite the tailor's shop.

1   VOICES. Very good, sir.

2   GOVERNOR. You Martin and Williams come with me. You three stay on duty at the gate here. Any others that arrive send them into the tailor's shop. Right, come on.

3   LENEGAN. Get cracking. If they get out in those streets they'll need a hell of a lot of finding. Will that be enough of the alarm, sir?

4   GOVERNOR. Yes. That'll do, Lenegan.

Alarm stops.

5   MARTIN. Look, sir, who's that up there?

6   WILLIAMS. It's them. Along the ledge of the tailor's shop.

7   GOVERNOR. You're right. [*Yells.*] Hi, up there, give yourself up, you're cornered.

8   WILLIAMS. There's the chief.

9   JENKINS [*yells, distant*]. Hi, you three. You might as well turn it in.

10 WILLIAMS. That's Tillotson running along the ledge.

11 MARTIN. He's making a dash for it, sir.

12 GOVERNOR. He can't get away from there.

13 MARTIN. He's going to jump for it, on to the top of the prison wall.

14 WILLIAMS. It's a ten foot jump and a forty foot drop if he misses. He'll never risk it.

15 JENKINS [*distant*]. Don't be a fool, Tillotson. You can't do it. Give yourself up, we've got your two mates.

16 DAVIS [*pitiful yell*]. Don't jump, Tilly! Don't!

17 GOVERNOR. He'll never do it.

There is a pause, and then the silence is broken by a scream, feet can be heard hitting the wall, a scraping sound, a body dropping, and a final thud.

18 DAVIS. Tilly! Tilly!

19 GOVERNOR. Martin, find the M.O. at once. Come on Williams.

1 JENKINS [*distant bellow*]. He's down there beside the flower bed!

Racing footsteps. TILLOTSON *can be heard moaning.*

2 GOVERNOR [*whisper*]. Tillotson . . . you should never have done it. Let me make your head comfortable.

3 TILLOTSON. Thanks, guv.

4 GOVERNOR. How do you feel?

5 TILLOTSON. Like I was broken in two. Have you a fag, sir?

6 GOVERNOR. Yes. One second.

A match is scraped. Tillotson gives a pained groan.

7 WILLIAMS. Too late, sir. He won't smoke no more.

There is a distant uproar of women's voices.

8 GOVERNOR. Where's that coming from?

9 WILLIAMS. Sounds like the women's section, sir.

After a pause we fade up on an uproar of women's voices. A heavy door slams, and the uproar dies down slightly.

10 PRESTON. Miss Mooney, the Governor.

11 MOONEY. Two hundred and twelve all correct, sir.

12 GOVERNOR. What's going on here?

13 MOONEY. The escape alarm set them all off. They heard all the shouting before the poor man jumped.

14 GOVERNOR. I've a good idea who's behind it all.

15 MOONEY. Yes, she started it off.

16 GOVERNOR. I've had enough for one night. Miss Preston, bring the hose-pipe along will you.

17 PRESTON. Yes, sir.

The uproar builds up. There is yelling, shouting, and some singing.

18 GOVERNOR. Let's go straight to her cell.

The uproar increases.

1   GOVERNOR. Miss Mooney, things seem to be getting out of hand over here.

2   MOONEY. It's just the din, sir. Not as bad as it sounds. Here we are. Let's look in on her.

The door slot is opened.

3   RUTH [*shouting*]. You've killed Tillotson. You dirty lot. You trapped him up there, and made him jump. You killed him. He only wanted a bit of freedom. But you dirty rotten bunch of screws drove him to his death.

Sounds of crashing come from the cell. There is a moment's silence and then a baby's wail is heard.

4   ADA. Ruth! Ruth love! Don't forget there's a baby.

Sudden silence.

5   RUTH. Sorry. I'm sorry Ada.

The baby's wailing dies away. Silence.

6   MOONEY. They're soon set off, soon quietened. You won't need the hose, Miss Preston.

Sound of the swivel slot again. A pause.

7   GOVERNOR. She looks very weary.

8   MOONEY. She's spent out, sir.

9   GOVERNOR. She's still got that spark of defiance. Even as she sits there.

10   MOONEY. That's her spirit, sir. I wouldn't like to see her lose that. It's something you need to get through life.

11   GOVERNOR. Yes, but it needs to go along the right way.

12   MOONEY. Yes, sir. That's what I'd like to see you about. Let's go into my office for a minute.

The door closes behind them.

13   GOVERNOR. Well, what is it?

14   MOONEY. Ruth goes out in three weeks, sir.

F

1 GOVERNOR. That's right. If I don't put another charge in against her. I'll be glad to see the last of her too.

2 MOONEY. It won't be the last of her if she goes out in that mood, with another three weeks brewing up.

3 GOVERNOR. I don't care how she goes out, so long as she goes. I did have hopes for her, but now I doubt if there is anything we can do. I don't believe that this orphan shock could have affected her so much.

4 MOONEY. I know what it means to have nobody. I grew up with it. She got it in one moment.

5 GOVERNOR. What was your suggestion?

6 MOONEY. If Ruth hadn't lost all her good conduct remission she would have left here some weeks ago.

7 GOVERNOR. Yes.

8 MOONEY. If you apply for the restoration of three weeks remission, on account of her good behaviour before she saw her parents, she could leave prison tomorrow.

9 GOVERNOR. You mean let her out?

10 MOONEY. Why not? It'll be a good shock, for a change.

11 GOVERNOR. I think it's a preposterous idea . . . but I'll take a chance on you, Mooney.

12 MOONEY. You won't be sorry. If the telegram went off tonight, you'd have an answer tomorrow morning. You could add my recommendation.

13 GOVERNOR. I certainly won't take responsibility myself. Goodnight.

Fade out.

Fade in on MOONEY *humming; there is a knock on the door.*

Come in.

14 PRESTON. Good morning, Miss Mooney.

15 MOONEY. Good morning. Lovely day.

1 PRESTON. Summer at last. Now what are we to do about Ruth Lawrence?

2 MOONEY. How is she this morning?

3 PRESTON. She is in her cell and looking very weary. But she is as defiant as ever. Singing away and making out she doesn't care a hang.

4 MOONEY. Does she . . . care?

5 PRESTON. I don't know. The cell is in a bad state . . . she did a lot of damage and we've left her amongst it.

6 MOONEY. It'll do her good.

7 PRESTON. Look who's coming across the yard. The Governor. At this hour of the morning.

8 MOONEY. Does he look pleased?

9 PRESTON. He's got his pokerface on him, but he's walking briskly. I'll see you later, Miss Mooney. [*She goes.*]

   A pause.

10 GOVERNOR. Good morning, Miss Mooney.

11 MOONEY. 212. All correct, sir. Good morning.

12 GOVERNOR. There's your telegram.

13 MOONEY [*reads*]. 'In answer to your application for the restoration of remission of sentence forfeited by Ruth Lawrence, we are glad to inform you that it has been granted . . .'

14 GOVERNOR. Now you can take it to her.

15 MOONEY. That's your job, sir.

Fade in on RUTH *humming cheerfully; the key turns in the lock, and she stops at once. The door opens.*

16 PRESTON. Prisoner Lawrence. The Governor to see you.

17 RUTH. Show him in, I know what he wants.

18 GOVERNOR. Good morning, Ruth.

19 RUTH. I'm ready—where are we going this time?

1   GOVERNOR. Read this.

2   RUTH. In answer to your application for the restoration of . . . [*Mumble.*] . . . What does it mean, sir?

3   GOVERNOR. It means you're free. You can leave prison this morning.

4   RUTH. Free . . .

5   GOVERNOR. Easy there, Ruth.

Fades out on RUTH *sobbing.*

Fade in again with RUTH *laughing brightly.*

6   PRESTON. What's the matter, Ruth?

7   RUTH. This skirt. It's that loose I might fall out of it.

8   PRESTON. You've been slimming, girl. Here's your egg and bacon, and a pot of tea. That'll help fill it out a bit.

9   RUTH. Mm! That smells good.

The door opens.

10   STONE. Hello, Preston.

11   PRESTON. Hello, Stone.

12   RUTH. Cup of tea, Miss Stone?

13   STONE. What! . . .

14   PRESTON. Don't you know her? It's Ruth Lawrence.

15   STONE. Where are you going?

16   RUTH. Out. Here's your tea. I'd like to say how sorry I am, Miss Stone, for all the trouble I gave you.

17   STONE. I never expected to hear you say sorry. Let's forgive and forget. You won't mind if I say, I hope I never see you again.

18   RUTH. I don't think you will see me again.

19   PRESTON. Ruth, Miss Mooney would like to see you.

20   MOONEY. Well, Ruth, you look fresh and rested after your bath!

1 RUTH. I feel it. Different from my first bath here! Remember?

2 MOONEY. I'm not likely to forget.

3 RUTH. I don't know how to thank you, Miss Mooney.

4 MOONEY. I'm thanked enough by that changed look in your face.

5 RUTH. It was the moment the Governor came into my cell —and I was expecting to go below—when instead he handed me the telegram of release. Something changed inside me.

6 MOONEY. That's grand. [*Pause.*] Ruth, we got in touch with your people this morning.

7 RUTH. With Mum and Dad! . . . Are they all right?

8 MOONEY. Yes, they're fine. And if you'd go back home to them, Ruth, they'd be very happy.

9 RUTH. Happy! . . . to have me . . . after all I've [*Intimate whisper.*] Miss Mooney, I can never thank you.

10 MOONEY. That new look on your face is all the thanks I want. Come on now, keep back the tears. Come along.

Fade out.

Fade in.

11 GOVERNOR. Mr. and Mrs. Lawrence . . . Ruth's in here. Let's go in.

12 MRS. LAWRENCE [*nervous*]. Do you think it will be all right this time, sir?

13 GOVERNOR. Absolutely! And any time in future. Wait till you see her.

14 MR. LAWRENCE. I had a feeling it would all come right, Mother.

The door opens.

Oh here's Miss Mooney.

1 MOONEY. Go on, in you go. Ruth's waiting.

2 MR. LAWRENCE. Go on Mother, I'm with you.

The door shuts, There is a pause.

3 MRS. LAWRENCE [*low, uncertain*]. Ruth . . .

4 RUTH. Mum! Oh Mum . . . [*They embrace, sobbing.*] My Mum.

5 MRS. LAWRENCE [*confident*]. Ruth love . . . Ruth love. [*Sobs.*]

6 MR. LAWRENCE. Ruthy . . . are you all right?

7 RUTH. Yes, Dad. . . . I'm all right now. [*Happy sobs.*]

Fade out

The Day Dumbfounded Got His Pylon

by Henry Livings

Cast:

DUMBFOUNDED

MRS. RUPERT SKERN

IM

BELCH

TELEPHONE OPERATOR

✳ ✳ ✳
The Day Dumbfounded
Got His Pylon

A suburban garden. Birds twitter in the background. An electric mower whirrs to a halt and then restarts.

1   DUMBFOUNDED [*calm mastery*]. Press the red button . . . uh, uh-huh. Blue button for approach . . . there's my beauty. You can keep your boats, I'm for an electric mower: the whirr of cold green steel over the gentle moist grass, ho hum, and me in my off-white stout canvas planished steel-framed loggia lounging support. Look at those men: that's forty minutes by the clock they've been there. Fine thing. *Fine thing.* Here she comes on the approach . . . press the red button . . once for turn and stand-by for re-start . . . and . . , [*Effort.*] once for stand-down.

The lawn mower stops.

What-are-they-about I should like to know? I'd just like to ask them, just what? Two men and a van. *Two.* [*Calls.*] Mrs. Skern! [*He moves away.*] Mrs. Skern, I should like you to tell me where my writing materials are, *if* you please. [*He moves into the house.*]
[*Approach.*] Ah. Handy on my escritoire. [*Calls.*] Mrs. Skern! Dearest! Don't trouble, I've found them!

2   MRS. SKERN [*distant*]. What is it, Rupert?

3   DUMBFOUNDED [*writing*]. Dear Sir, I am dumbfounded . . . Oh yes, the date: from that they will know it was Saturday today. [*Recap.*] Dear Sir, I am dumbfounded. That on a Saturday morning . . . two workmen can spend not less than forty minutes standing in an estate van. Sitting in an estate van. In an estate van standing in a suburban by-way paragraph . . . I wonder what this labour, 'labour' will cost their employer? or what

he will gain? And I wonder too, will they go home to their electrically washed and spin-dried wives and say, they've had a *hard week of it*? Aha. And ho hum. [*Pause.*]

A car door slams and we hear the scrunch of approaching boots.

[*Musical with cunning.*] Ah. *Now* they come. I'll find out their business. Great healthy fellows, duffle-coated, caps ratting and [*Pause.*] instruments. The second one looks markedly senile . . . typical that he should be carrying the heavy . . . tripod thing. Old father time nh nh. Why a theodolite? [*Recede.*] Shut the door.

He shuts the door quickly.

[*With rising tension.*] Let them knock. Respectfully. Politely. I can observe them from here. [*Pause. Controlled nerves.*] Mrs. Skern! There are two men, workmen, duffle coats and ratting caps and instruments, instruments, look out of the bedroom window! They're laying them down and setting them up, a Primus stove why should they want a Primus stove? and a theolodite thelodomite!

2 MRS. SKERN [*distant.*] Yes? What is it, Rupert? They're on the escritoire!

3 DUMBFOUNDED. They're retiring. Hadn't the nerve . . . Their nerve failed them . . . To come to my door

The car door slams.

They've left their instruments. [*Watching hard.*] Look here, they're using my garden as if it were, as if it were the Botanicals and Public.

He opens the interior door.

[*Hisses.*] Look out of the bedroom window!

4 MRS. SKERN [*nearer now*]. Stakes!

5 DUMBFOUNDED. What?

1 MRS. SKERN. Stakes!!

He scampers across the room and closes the interior door then scampers back and wrenches the outer door open.

2 DUMBFOUNDED [*swallowing a shout*]. Hey! you! him! What d'you think you're doing? You're intruding!

He shuts the outer door quickly. Panic breathing.

3 MRS. SKERN. Stakes and ropes!!

4 DUMBFOUNDED. I'm not going out to them. Fine thing. [*Calls.*] A fine thing, Mrs. Skern! They've clearly been given an incorrect address! And they haven't the natural born intelligence to enquire of the owner! Poor material! A quite unwarranted intrusion.

5 MRS. SKERN [*distant*]. Yes, dear?

6 DUMBFOUNDED. Poor material!

7 MRS. SKERN Yes, dear? Just a minute I'm coming down.

He picks up the writing paper.

8 DUMBFOUNDED [*reads*]. . . . nn-dried wives and say that they've had a hard week of it . . . mm . . . [*Writes.*] '. . . but this is not all. After contemplation worthy of Tibetan lamas they finally hit on *my* garden as the scene for further repose . . . Unaware or uncaring that their services . . . their 'services' were neither ordered nor required. Ar um. Ah! [*Sarcastic.*] He *approaches.* [*Writes.*] Finally the senior intellect approached . . .

There is a knock at the door. DUMBFOUNDED *hastily thrusts back his chair and pulls open the door.*

9 MRS. SKERN [*close*]. Who is it, dearest?

10 DUMBFOUNDED. Aah!

11 MRS. SKERN [*suppressed hysteria*]. I can't bear workmen in the house.

12 DUMBFOUNDED. Ah, oh it's you. Dearest, it's the workmen, dearest, no harm. [*To the intruder.*] What d'you want?

1   IM [*shouting off to his mate*]. It's all right they've answered! [*To* DUMBFOUNDED.] Kettleful of water.

2   DUMBFOUNDED. I am dumbfounded. Dumbfounded.

3   IM. That right?

4   MRS. SKERN [*genteel condescension*]. I'm *Mrs*. Skern.

5   IM. How d'you do? Can we have a kettle full of water?

6   DUMBFOUNDED. That's enough. You'll be telling me next you had a hard week of it.

7   IM. Aye, we have.

8   DUMBFOUNDED [*rising pressure*]. You've not been here five seconds when here you are demanding kettles of water.

9   IM. We've been here a while.

10   DUMBFOUNDED. I *know* you have! Isn't that just it exactly? I've got your number, oh yes. *I've already written*. I know all I need to know. What's your name?

11   IM. Im.

12   DUMBFOUNDED. What authority do you work for? What's that?

13   IM. Eh?

14   DUMBFOUNDED [*firm, icy*]. I seem to remember asking you your name.

15   IM. Im.

16   DUMBFOUNDED. If that is intended as insolence I will pass over it. Do you intend to tell me your employer's name?

17   IM. We hung about because you were mowing and what we have to do might have disturbed you.

18   DUMBFOUNDED. Your employer's name, if you please. What do you mean, disturb?

19   IM. Digging about on your lawn.

20   DUMBFOUNDED [*wild*]. Will you, once and for all, tell me who you work for?

MRS. SKERN *screams briefly*.

162

1 IM. Electricity.

2 DUMBFOUNDED. Disturb me? Digging up my lawn? You've found the right word, haven't you! *Disturb* me? You've succeeded! By heaven, you've made a first class job of it!

3 IM. Now it's not my fault.

4 DUMBFOUNDED. Make no doubt of it, it's not going to happen.

5 IM. Nothing to do with me.

6 DUMBFOUNDED. Disturbed I am, yes, dumbfounded as well, but there'll be no digging, *no* digging, not digging in my lawn, oh my word no. Not a bit.

7 IM. You'll have to speak to someone else about that.

There is a distant belch. DUMBFOUNDED *slams the door.*

8 MRS. SKERN. Rupert! You might have trapped his kettle in the door.

9 DUMBFOUNDED [*wondering*]. I'll swear that . . . that decrepit old man . . . standing out there by the copper beech . . . I'll swear he . . . belched. I can't believe it's happening to me . . . it wouldn't happen to anyone else, would it?

10 MRS. SKERN [*whisper*]. He's still there.

11 DUMBFOUNDED. Got him now. *He* doesn't know what to do. [*Calmer.*] Pretty effective sabotage, eh? No water, no tea, no tea, no digging. [*Pause.*]

A boot scrunches outside.

Poor material.

12 Mrs. Skern. Seems a bit rude, Rupert, after all it *is* elevenses.

13 DUMBFOUNDED. Serve 'em right.

14 MRS. SKERN. And they have been waiting a long time. You didn't have to be rude, not after they waited for you to finish mowing the lawn [*Trailing off.*] before they dug . . . it up.

DUMBFOUNDED *gives a moan of anxiety. He opens the door.*

1 IM [*outside*]. It's the kettle . . .

> *He closes it again quickly.*

2 DUMBFOUNDED. Still there.

3 MRS. SKERN. Go and tell him off.

4 DUMBFOUNDED. Stop trying to make me *do* things.

5 MRS. SKERN. I am not trying to make you do things.

6 DUMBFOUNDED. Yes you are, you said . . . what was it that you just said?

7 MRS. SKERN. I am merely trying to make some constructive suggestion. I mean we don't *want* two men with instruments . . . stakes and ropes and such . . . in the garden, do we? [*Rising hysteria.*] We don't actually *want* them there, you must admit that at least!

8 DUMBFOUNDED [*tense*]. Be quiet, be quiet. Now. They're stymied for the time being . . . ah! Yes. I can get along with my letter. Make a pretty firm letter of it. That's the first thing . . .

9 MRS. SKERN. Listen . . .

10 DUMBFOUNDED. . . . while they're hung up. You've got to be firm with these fellows. Let them know who they're dealing with, someone who can *react*. It's the only language they understand. Who pays the rates, mm? Answer me that?

> *The sound of water running into a kettle outside.*

Betrayed by my own standpipe. [*Recedes.*] By *heavens*, Mrs. Skern, by heck.

> *He picks up the phone.*

Ho hum.

11 OPERATOR. Number please.

12 DUMBFOUNDED. I want the electricity board. They're using my standpipe without so much as a by your leave, and that's not all.

> *A pause.*

1 OPERATOR. You haven't got that quite right, have you, caller? [*In a professional voice.*] D'you want the Water Board Night Emergencies?

2 DUMBFOUNDED. I shall expect the sky to fall. These, my dearest, are what we fondly imagine are *our* public services.

3 MRS. SKERN [*admonition*]. Oh really, Rupert.

4 OPERATOR. Number, please.

5 DUMBFOUNDED. Oh yes 'number, please', eh? Not a millimetre from the path of strict obligation, I notice.

6 OPERATOR. I beg your pardon, caller?

7 DUMBFOUNDED. Do you, indeed?

8 OPERATOR. Do you wish Post Office Telephone Complaints or Water Board Night Emergencies? [*Sotto.*] Right nana we've got here Doris.

9 DUMBFOUNDED [*shouts*]. What in heaven's name should I want with Water Board Night Emergencies at eleven o'clock on a Saturday morning?

10 OPERATOR. I beg your pardon, caller, I was under the impression that you had some trouble with your standpipe. I think you'd better go out to a call box and use the emergency call system, they have people to deal with people like you.

11 DUMBFOUNDED. I do not *want* night emergencies, with any board, on a Saturday morning!

12 OPERATOR. It's always Night Emergencies on Saturday morning, so snorts.

He slams the phone down; then picks it up again.

13 DUMBFOUNDED. Hallo! Hallo!

14 OPERATOR. Number, please, oh it's you again, is it?

15 DUMBFOUNDED. Get the Electricity Board, at once!

16 OPERATOR. Number, please.

17 DUMBFOUNDED. Eh?

18 OPERATOR. What number?

1 DUMBFOUNDED. Oh my heavens. [*He leaps through the directory.*] What number?... What number? You mean you don't know? Aren't you employed to know numbers? If this is the way the Board normally carries on you must get thousands of calls for them. You know Morton Fanbeater's number right enough when I phone seven p.m. every Thursday to discuss matters appertaining to the Friday horticultural evening!

2 OPERATOR. That's Phyllis, I don't do evenings, by my husband's desire.

3 DUMBFOUNDED [*savage*]. Then how do you know about my calls to Morton Fanbeater?

4 OPERATOR. I'm afraid I can't discuss that with a subscriber.

An electric saw starts up in the garden.

5 DUMBFOUNDED. Mrs. Skern! What are they doing?

6 MRS. SKERN [*straining to see*]. I don't think I'm sure, I think it may be a saw thing, dearest, but you mustn't excite yourself so.

7 DUMBFOUNDED. What are they *doing*? No, don't tell me, I prefer my ignorance. [*On phone.*] Get me the Electricity Board, they've got an electric saw now!

8 OPERATOR. You're doing it again, aren't you, caller? Number, please.

9 DUMBFOUNDED. Must we suffer the inconveniences of a manual exchange and enjoy no advantage?

10 OPERATOR. S'matter of fact I do know the number of the Electricity Board and if you hadn't been so rotten rude I might have put you through.

DUMBFOUNDED *groans and flings the directory down.*

11 DUMBFOUNDED. 2965!

12 OPERATOR [*like a Cash Register*]. Wrong!

13 DUMBFOUNDED. 2695.

14 OPERATOR. Wrong!

166

1   DUMBFOUNDED. I give up, what is it?

2   OPERATOR. 9625?

3   DUMBFOUNDED [*struggling*]. Get me 9625. Please.

4   OPERATOR. Wrong!

5   DUMBFOUNDED. Ah!

6   MRS. SKERN. Really, Mr. Skern, sometimes you are quite rude with people. [*On phone.*] Hallo? Yes, of course, silly of me, the number I want. [*She leafs through the directory.*] Mm? There, dearest, the young lady sends her regards and says she was just beginning to enjoy herself. Ah: 2-a-5-a-9-a-6-a. Thank you. Oh no, I think he's been overworking, you know, mm. My number? 2-a-5-a. Hallo? Electricity Board? [*We hear the distant voice of an official trying to get a word in.*] Now don't start telling me a long story before I've even started, there's a dear man. Two of your men are digging up our lawn. Will you kindly hold the line and I'll call him . . . because you must tell him to stop it . . . [*She opens the window.*] I say! Mr. Im! Will you be so good as to come in here and speak to your superior! I have him on the line! there you are, you see, dearest: civility costs nothing and works wonders and please don't bite your nails. [*On phone.*] He's coming now . . . It may be their job but you must tell him to stop it . . . I daresay, but it disturbs my husband. No, I can't accept that, I *know* you have your job to do, you said so . . . You! Whoever you are don't you dare put the phone down! My name is Lady Bracknell and I once launched a ship. Don't deceive me, I know enough about Power Stations to be aware that they don't, as you so picturesquely put it, 'grind to a cathedral stillness' because a few silly dials are spinning in the wrong direction.

There is a knock at the door.

7   MRS. SKERN. Let Mr. Im in, please, dearest.

He opens the door.

1   IM [*approaching*]. We're having a bit of trouble with that flowering cherry.

2   DUMBFOUNDED. Flowering cherry? What's he getting at? I haven't got . . . he means my copper beech!

3   IM. Aye, that'll be it; it's got damn big roots has that. [*On phone.*] Hallo?

4   DUMBFOUNDED. Roots?

5   MRS. SKERN [*sotto*]. Dearest, do be civil.

6   IM. Yes, Yis, Mr. Inge. Right. No, no more, not no more' you won't. No, quite the contrary, they've been co-operative with us, only a bit of shouting, that's all.

7   MRS. SKERN. There you are, you see, dearest?

8   DUMBFOUNDED. What does that mean, roots? I daren't look.

9   IM. Well you get off home then, I should, soon as you can. [*He replaces the phone. Approaching.*] You want to be very careful, missis, how you speak to Mr. Inge, he's got a funny temperament. You got him in quite a state there; thought his wife had put you on to him. [*Recede.*] I'll let myself out.

10   MRS. SKERN. I hope he told you?

11   IM. I think you should know, Mrs, Skern, that there's ways and ways of doing things, proper charnels and *im*proper charnels. Now, *if* you'll excuse me, I'll get back to my work, for which I am paid for.

12   MRS. SKERN [*faint*]. Anything we can do?

13   IM [*heavy*]. A screw of tea, I think, might be a kind thought. Pig ignorant.

     He closes the door as he goes. MRS. SKERN *sobs heavily.*

14   DUMBFOUNDED. There, there, Mrs. Skern, you weren't to know.

15   MRS. SKERN. I didn't *mean* to upset him.

16   DUMBFOUNDED. Of course you didn't.

17   MRS. SKERN. Oh do stop *agreeing* all the time!

1   DUMBFOUNDED. Sorry.

2   MRS. SKERN. And *look* at the floor, *look* where his boots have been!

3   DUMBFOUNDED. Yes, dearest, I'll sweep it up.

4   MRS. SKERN. Don't leave me!

5   DUMBFOUNDED. I'm only going for the dustpan and brush, dearest.

6   MRS. SKERN [*tears*]. There you are, you're being patient with me, I knew you would!

He starts to brush the floor.

I'm so unhappy; how can men be so gross? We never did anything to them.

7   DUMBFOUNDED [*brushing*]. The working man nowadays has to be handled with a great deal of psychology, Mrs. Skern. They've got the upper hand, at least they think they have, and they know it. Feather-bedded; if we say one word out of turn to either of those two out there, d'you know we'd probably have a strike on our hands? You do realize that? They have to be treated with the utmost delicacy, those louts, and they must never be made aware that good breeding conceals natural authority . . .

He becomes aware of the sound of iron stakes being driven into the ground with a sled.

[*Rushing to the door.*] What in heaven's name are they up to now?

8   MRS. SKERN. Rupert! Be careful! Remember what we said!

He wrenches open the door.

9   DUMBFOUNDED. They are attacking the very roots, [*Winces.*] the very foundations of what little meaning I have left in my life! I can't remember anything!

10   IM. That's called amnesia.

Final clunk of sled.

There, that's pretty firm. Take a bit of driving in, these stakes, you must have a rocky bed; where d'you want your sundial?

2   DUMBFOUNDED [*babbling*]. Very decent of you to ask, but I'm quite happy with it where it is, strategically placed in the small rose arbour where it catches the sun's rays throughout the day and at all seasons of the year. [*Growing less certain.*] . . . I'll keep it in the small rose arbour.

3   IM [*comfy*]. Hmph. Sun. There's not much of that about, I shouldn't think.

4   DUMBFOUNDED. Oh, I don't know, we get . . . where is it?

5   IM. Where's what?

6   DUMBFOUNDED. My rose arbour, there's no rose arbour any more, it's not about, it's nowhere to be seen.

7   IM. No, that's right; I was wondering when you'd get around to noticing that. I was sorry about that myself, being a gardner in my own small way . . .

8   DUMBFOUNDED. Perished! As though it had never been!

9   IM. I didn't like doing it, I can tell you, with it being in bloom and all, felt like a murderer.

10 DUMBFOUNDED. The grass groweth and withereth away . . .

11 IM. Aye, well, you have got some of that yet.

12 DUMBFOUNDED. Silence! Be quiet! You chat away like some foul old woman, knitting as the heads roll!

13 IM. We had these four *stakes*, d'you see? *One at each corner*, d'you see? And your lawn isn't exactly *square*, d'you see? That was our trouble; not *square* as the book reads square, not with that rose arbour like taking a bite out of the top end, nibbling at the quadrilateral, that's why I asked you about the sundial, for the hightth as well.

14 DUMBFOUNDED. The hightth?

15 IM. Yes, the sundial is too high for the purpose, though we could use the plinth, that's be all right for the hightth. Quite tragic to see, isn't it? All those delicate petals,

strewn, as it were, broadcast. Have you got a use for those copper beech logs? Because if you haven't, I'll take them off your hands.

IM'S *assistant starts to rock the sundial on it's foundation.*

2   DUMBFOUNDED [*shouting*]. No! No! No! Leave the sundial! Leave me that. What are you trying to do? Stop that! [*The old man belches.*] How dare you! [*He belches again.*] Don't do that! [*Pause.*] Heavens, he's going to do it again . . . no he isn't.

3   IM [*approaching*]. You'll get no conversation out of him.

4   DUMBFOUNDED. Mr. Im, what is this fellow's name?

5   IM. Him?

6   DUMBFOUNDED. Stop that, I won't have it, d'you hear? This man is insolent: he . . . broke wind . . . with insolence. In reply to a perfectly civil request. [*Shouts.*] Leave that sundial where it is, sir! [*Calmer.*] Look, gentlemen, won't you, both of you, please come and have a cup of tea with my lady wife and myself? And let us at least *discuss* this, like civilised people. I know your kettle is boiling on that neat little portable Primus you seem to have brought, and I don't want you to think I *mind* my syringa being scorched and then steamed . . .
[*Another Belch.*]

7   IM. Talks like management, doesn't he? Now you listen to me: you talk about being civilised, and haven't I just seen and heard you calling that poor old man . . .

8   DUMBFOUNDED. Do I have to explain in words of one syllable that that sundial was a very expensive item?

9   IM. . . . calling, I say, a bald and toothless old man who's trying to hold down a good job in spite of his disability *for which none of your sort will allow him so much as a threepence-worth of pension*?

10 DUMBFOUNDED [*doesn't think to like what the answer will be*]. Disability?

11 IM. Flatulence. He's got flatulence.

1 DUMBFOUNDED. My wife will develop alopecia if this morning doesn't stop soon. I know what he's got!

2 IM. Flatulence.

3 DUMBFOUNDED. Insolence!

4 IM. Flatulence . . .

5 DUMBFOUNDED. Stop saying that.

6 IM. . . . and it makes him shy of speaking in case he . . . [*He belches again.*] there he goes again, poor old crampus; we call him foul pest. [BELCH *struggles to move the sundial.*] You see? You can stand there and watch him toil, can't you?

7 DUMBFOUNDED. Oh. Now, Mr. er er . . .

8 IM. Call him Foul Pest, he doesn't mind, makes him feel people are being friendly.

9 DUMBFOUNDED. You mustn't attempt that by yourself . . . [*Straining.*] Where d'you suggest?

10 IM. Oh well now, well, I suppose that's more up to you, isn't it? It being your garden.

11 DUMBFOUNDED. Say somewhere, quick!

12 IM. What about over there?

13 DUMBFOUNDED [*in agony*]. Croci.

14 IM. There?

15 DUMBFOUNDED [*choking*]. Daffs. It's no good, I'll have to lay it down.

16 IM [*urgent*]. Don't set your legs apart! No, don't bend your back!

17 DUMBFOUNDED. How the devil am I to lay it down without somehow getting my hands somewhere near the ground? [*Sudden gasp and give.*] Aaah! My finger end!

18 IM. It's easy to see you've never done any humping before.

19 DUMBFOUNDED. Is that a crime? Get it off, get it off, get it off. [*Relief.*] Oh. Oh thank heavens.

20 IM. It's not a crime, but you have to admit you see things differently.

1 DUMBFOUNDED. Oh yes, of course, bound to. Capital and labour.

2 IM. I was thinking more of idiots and those who can work. You know that was just my way of testing you out, getting you at that stone; next time you see an old gaffer heaving at his work you'll be more circumspect, won't you? [*Genial chuckle.*] Old Foul wasn't daft enough to get lumbered with Stone Henge, but guess who was?

3 DUMBFOUNDED. Don't you care what sort of an impression you make on me?

4 IM. I *know* what sort of an impression I'm going to make on you.

5 DUMBFOUNDED [*nervous*]. Oh yes? A pleasant impression, I hope?

6 IM. You see. You'll be chuffed, take my word for it, choked.

7 DUMBFOUNDED. Happy?

8 IM. Well, put it this way: that last feller we fitted one on, still writes to us.

9 DUMBFOUNDED. Fitted one on?

10 IM. That's it. He wants us to send him photographs of me and Foul Pest. Now will you take hold of this rope end and take a turn round that stake. [*Going away.*] Foul, you take it to the far stake, and I'll do the other two.

11 DUMBFOUNDED. Won't that rope off the entire garden?

12 IM [*off*]. You'll have the path to come and go. It's only temporary.

13 DUMBFOUNDED [*calls*]. Temporary? Till when?

14 IM [*distant shout*]. Till we've finished building the pylon!

15 DUMBFOUNDED. Take a turn round the stake. Till we've finished building . . . the what? . . . Till we've finished . . . building . . . the . . . PYLON!!

16 IM [*shouting*]. That's right, the electric pylon!

    A tea-tray jingles in the distance.

17 MRS. SKERN [*calling brightly*]. Tea, everyone?

1   DUMBFOUNDED [*breathless, sotto, feverish*]. You must on no
    account mention this in front of Mrs. Skern. One
    rough word and she's had more than she can take,
    alopecia. I'll break it to her, tell her in my own way.

2   IM. Oh? [*Stage whisper.*] Oh yes, you want it to be your sur-
    prise, eh? You'll be proud to have it, sir.

3   DUMBFOUNDED. Silence ... or by heavens I'll ... rive you
    with one of your own stakes.

4   MRS. SKERN [*haughty*]. Now then, Rupert. Tea, old man? Tea,
    Mr. Im?

    The old man guggles his tea.

5   MRS. SKERN [*strained*]. Now yours, dearest. [*Sotto.*] The old man
    is gargling with it, dearest, he truly is.

    The old man belches. MRS. SKERN *drops the cup and saucer which
    smash on the paving.*

6   MRS. SKERN [*brave*]. Silly me.

7   DUMBFOUNDED. Mrs. Skern, that was my mother's Spode.

8   MRS. SKERN [*snap*]. I *know* whose Spode it was. [*Gay.*] Silly me,
    I'll clear it up.

    She picks up the morsels of china.

9   IM. That old stuff: they didn't have the know-how in
    those days. Look at this cup, all cracks. We've had
    nothing but plastic in our house ever since they first
    came out.

10 MRS. SKERN. Oh, Mr. Im, you're such an original.

11 DUMBFOUNDED. Those happen to be genuine Spode, nearly
    two hundred years old.

12 IM. Aye they are, aren't they. Ever since the first ones that
    used to go all floppy with hot tea so 't made like little
    spouts all round the rim. We had many a laugh over
    tea, spurting tea all over the cloth. We're humorous
    that way in our house.

1   MRS. SKERN. I'm sure that must have been very nice for you; would you like to put your teacup on the tray for me if you've finished?

IM *puts his cup and saucer on to the tray.*

Thank you. Now yours, dearest. You know you do look odd.

2   DUMBFOUNDED [*rapidly and very quietly*]. These gentlemen are going to build a pylon in our garden, dearest. It will take up the area of the lawn, though it will, of course, let in light, including the rose arbour and we shall still have the side path. I *am* writing a firm letter, you know that, don't you?

3   IM. You'll have no bother with it, it doesn't need tending, and you'll find it handy of a washing day.

4   MRS. SKERN [*dazed*]. I have a washing machine, with drier.

5   DUMBFOUNDED. . . . a very strong letter, it starts I am dumbfounded because as you know I shall be fully occupied on Monday and it's Night Emergency at the Electricity Board on Saturday mornings.

6   IM. If you take to swinging about on it, wear rubber boots, and don't allow any part of your body to earth you. It'll fry you else. I don't know if you've a fancy for that sort of thing. Some do.

7   DUMBFOUNDED. Mrs. Skern, speak, you must speak, to ease your mind. I had to tell you, dearest, I couldn't let you just find out . . . you'd never have forgiven me. [*Violent.*] You swine! This experience could be traumatic for my wife.

8   IM. Now *then,* sir . . .

9   DUMBFOUNDED. Look at her! Her lips are blue!

10   IM. Aye, they are, aren't they. Eh, but listen, you can't take up this attitude: would you have us laying *underground* where every spit you dig in your garden is a nightmare of apprehension? We've got to have power, you know that. And what about your rocky bed?

11   DUMBFOUNDED. What about it?

1 IM. We'd have to blast.

2 DUMBFOUNDED. I just can't bear to see her looking like that. Dearest! Like a sheep.

3 IM. You're quite happy to accept the amenities, I notice, but will you accept the liabilities, the duties My little villa, modest as it is, stands across the road from a gasometer, but do I complain? Oh, no, I *like* it, it's little ups and downs entertain and instruct my children. Electric radio, light, electronic television B.B.C. channel only, electric photocell eyes oh yes, but *pylons* no!

4 DUMBFOUNDED [*pity me*]. Why *my* garden?

5 IM. Oh yes, the old story, 'what *me*?' The garden goes to him who can use it best. Here [*He opens up the plans.*] take a look. That's how it'll be. That's the elevation, it's more or less the same all round, you see?

In the distance the hum of a power cable, with wind, gradually mounting in volume.

And here's the plan. And down the side here are sections of the various parts. That's an insulator, wouldn't believe they were as big as that, would you? Superb constructions. Wish I had one.

6 DUMBFOUNDED. Can you hear anything?

7 IM. Ah, you're impressed. I knew you would be.

8 DUMBFOUNDED. Yes, yes, it's noble. Are you sure you can't, like a sort . . . a sort of humming?

9 IM. Power that is, high tension power.

10 DUMBFOUNDED. Oh, I'm tense all right. I think I'll go in. Come along, dearest.

The trayful of china crashes on the paving.

Leave that, we'll go inside. Are you sure you can't hear anything?

11 MRS. SKERN. Silly, dearest, I didn't say I couldn't, of course I can hear something, that humming.

1 DUMBFOUNDED. It's modern industrial power, dearest, and domestic too, of course, though to a lesser extent. D'you think I could have a further look at that document?

2 IM. You can have it, I've got another.

3 DUMBFOUNDED. Oh, oh, I say that's good of you. I would like to have it up on the wall. In my den, you know. [*Recede.*] I don't know, Mrs. Skern, but I imagine the fellows in the club will jest about this, without fully understanding. But then they would have laughed at Bleriot. Probably did.

He opens the door. The humming slowly fades.

Shall we have the wireless on? for a little music?

He closes the door. The humming stops.

4 IM. Come on now, Foul Pest, don't stand there gawping with the only bit of Skern Spode extant clutched in your nerveless hand; there's holes to be dug, elevations to be read and intervals to be measured. And you can take that kettle off, Mr. Skern's syringa should be done by now. I wonder if we rebuilt that sundial upside down it'd tell the time in Australia?

DUMBFOUNDED *throws open the window.*

5 DUMBFOUNDED. I say! Im! We're getting quite a clear reception on our little wireless!

The wireless plays a jaunty tune with a strong background of interference. Hum of cables and wind.

6 IM. You get some right nutters, you really do.

Fade out

Topics for Class Discussion

and Written Work

The Mating Season

1   What impression do you get from the first scene of the play of Stan's family and of his life?

2   What is the difference between Jack's and Stan's attitude towards girls?

3   Do you find Stan a likeable person?

4   How is it that Jack is able to forecast so accurately every move that Eileen makes?

5   At the end of the play Stan's mother says she was surprised to hear that Jack's wife was pregnant before their marriage. Were you surprised?

6   How does the author make you feel about the world of Stan, Jack, and the Palais? Is it attractive, and if so why?

7   When Stan eventually gets married, do you think his home life will be very different from that of his parents?

8   When he hears the news about Eileen's regular boy-friend (page 30 speech 21), Stan might have reacted in a different way. Write your version of the end of this play.

9   A voice inside a character's head is often used in radio plays, and can be very effective. How would you represent Jack if you were producing the play in the theatre?

The Dock Brief

1. What is meant by a 'Dock Brief'?

2. Why is Morgenhall so anxious to defend Fowle?

3. Why did Fowle advertise for a lodger with a sense of humour?

4. Why is Fowle reluctant to explain the reason for his reprieve?

5. The barrister enjoys using legal phraseology which his client cannot understand. How could the language used by the legal profession be simplified?

6. The author suggests by his portrayal of Morgenhall and Fowle that lawyers and criminals have a close affinity. Give your reasons for agreeing or disagreeing with him.

7. Would this play gain from being produced for Television or the Theatre rather than in its present form? Would anything be lost in the process?

8. Suggest an alternative title for the play.

Don't Wait for Me

1   Do you think that a man can go on loving a childhood sweetheart until they are both middle aged?

2   Looking back, Liz says 'You had your chances. Why didn't you take them?' *(page 105 speech 12)* Was there any likelihood of her agreeing to marry Eddie in their youth? Why didn't they marry? In spite of Eddie's devotion, why does she still reject him?

3   By the time we meet her in the play Liz is a pathetic person. How has she come to squander her life?

4   Is there anything about Liz as she is now that is in any way attractive?

5   Why does the author tell the story in a series of flashbacks and not in a straightforward manner from the beginning?

6   Why does the author bring in the character of the old lady in the fish shop?

7   Liz calls the sympathetic Eddie an 'insensitive lump'. What does she mean? Do you feel any pity for him, or do you think he is a fool?

8   Write a last speech for Eddie revealing what he feels when Liz goes away at the end of the play.

G

She'll Make Trouble

1   Why is Ruth a troublemaker?

2   Everyone finds something likeable in Ruth, and we are told that she is clever. Can you imagine a person who is completely unlikeable? Could a play have been written with that sort of person as the main character?

3   In what ways is Mooney a good prison officer?

4   What brings Ruth to her senses towards the end of the play?

5   Do you think that the author presents a true picture of life in prison?

6   The author might possibly have kept Tillotson alive, and ended the play with a romance between him and Ruth after they had left prison. Would this have been a better ending?

7   Write the report that the Governor might have written in the prison records describing Ruth's period of imprisonment.

The Day Dumbfounded
Got His Pylon

1. Most of the play consists of speeches by Dumbfounded.
   Mrs. Skern, and Im. How do their various ways of
   speaking show what sort of people they are?

2. Dumbfounded calls Im 'poor material' *(page 163 speech
   11)*, and Im calls Dumbfounded 'a right nutter' *(page
   177 speech 6)*. Do you agree with them both? Have you
   any sympathy for Dumbfounded?

3. Whenever Im and Dumbfounded are talking together,
   they do not seem really to understand each other. Do
   you agree that this is true and, if so, why do you think
   the author has made their characters like this?

4. Im accuses Dumbfounded of being quite happy to
   accept the amenities but not prepared to accept the
   liabilities. What does he mean?

5. By choosing this title for the play the author has
   deliberately given the game away, and the audience is
   one jump ahead of the leading character. Does this
   make the play less effective and amusing?

6. Write a letter to a paper complaining about the building
   of a large secondary school on land adjoining your
   well-kept garden. Sign the letter 'Outraged'.

General

1   These plays were all specially written for radio: find places where the author has used the special advantages of radio production to good effect.

2   Both *The Dock Brief* and *She'll Make Trouble* are about conflicts with the law. What are the attitudes of the two writers towards criminals? Have they anything in common?

3   Most of the writers in this volume come from the North of England; you might have guessed this in many cases, from the language, but can you find any other ways in which the background of the authors is shown in the plays?

4   If you decided to produce one of these plays on the stage, which would you choose? What alterations would you have to make to the text, and how would you arrange the production?

The Authors and their Work

ALAN PLATER

Alan Plater was born in Jarrow in 1935, but has lived in Hull since 1938. He studied architecture at King's College, Newcastle-upon-Tyne, but did not qualify. After a short period in an architect's office he started working on his own and was able to combine his interest in architecture with writing. His first play, *The Smokeless Zone*, was broadcast in 1961 and since then he has had four radio plays and six television plays produced. He has written two plays *Ted's Cathedral* and *A Smashing Day* for the theatre, and four of his radio and television plays have been adapted for the stage. He retains a strong interest in architecture, edits a literary programme for the BBC, and has written many episodes for the 'Z Cars' series.

JOHN MORTIMER

John Mortimer was born in 1923 and educated at Harrow and Oxford. He worked as an Assistant Director and later as a Script Writer in the Crown Film Unit. In 1948 he qualified as a barrister and while practising at the Bar completed six novels. *The Dock Brief*, his first play, was written for radio and won the coveted Italia Prize. He no longer writes novels but concentrates on writing for the theatre and cinema.

In addition to writing several sketches for revues, his work for the stage includes *I Spy* (Elek), *What Shall We Tell Caroline* (Elek), *The Wrong Side of the Park* (Heinemann), *Two Stars for Comfort* (Methuen) and *Lunch Hour* (Methuen). His television play *David and Broccoli* is available for schools in *Conflicting Generations* (Longmans).

DAVID CAMPTON

David Campton was born in 1924, and says that his only academic distinction was that he sat next to Richard Attenborough for two years. After spending three years as a flight mechanic in the R.A.F., he worked in the stores department of the Leicester Education Committee (in charge of caretakers' cleaning materials), and in 1949 became a clerk for the East Midlands Gas Board. In 1956 he decided to sink or swim as a full-time writer, and every play he has written since then has been produced somewhere or other.

His plays include *Sunshine on the Righteous*, *The Laboratory*, *Out of the Flying Pan* (included in *New Directions* published by Hutchinson), *A Soldier from the Wars Returning*, *Memento Mori*, *A Smell of Burning* and *Then . . .* (included in *Theatre Today* published by Longmans).

BILL NAUGHTON

Bill Naughton was born in Ireland but moved to Bolton when he was five years old. He left school when he was fourteen and went to work in a factory as a weaver. He did not like working under a roof, or having his boss too close at hand, so took up a job as a lorry driver and began to write in his spare time. After working as a labourer, a salesman and a hod-carrier, he had his first literary success in 1944 when *A Roof Over Your Head* was published. (It is now available in an educational edition published by Blackie.) He has written twenty radio plays, one of which, *Wigan to Rome*, has the distinction of being broadcast in the Home Service, Third and Light Programmes. His other work includes an autobiographical novel *One Small Boy*, and two volumes of short stories *Late Night on Watling Street* (Longmans) and *The Goal-keeper's Revenge* (Heinemann) and three successful stage plays *Alfie*, *All in Good Time* and *Spring and Port Wine*.

HENRY LIVINGS

Henry Livings was born in 1929. After leaving Grammar School he commenced a University Honours Course in Hispanic Studies at Liverpool but gave up after two years to wriggle his way into the theatre. He worked as a knitting-machine operator, pastry cook and railway goods porter to earn money to subsidize his first under-paid job as an assistant stage manager. He has acted with repertory companies in Leicester, Coventry and Sheffield and with the Century Theatre. His television plays include *Jack's 'Orrible Luck*, *The Arson Squad*, *There's No Room For You Here For a Start* (published by Methuen), *Nil Carborundum* and *A Right Crusader*. He has had five plays produced in the theatre: *Stop It Whoever you Are* (Penguin New Drama 5), *Nil Carborundum* (Penguin New Drama 6); *Big Soft Nellie*, *Kelly's Eye*, and *Eh!* (all published by Methuen). He is interested in acting and writing for radio. Apart from two original radio plays, *After the Last Lamp* and *The Day Dumbfounded Got His Pylon*, he has adapted Hauptmann's *The Weavers* and Ibsen's *An Enemy of the People*.

Producing Sound Drama in Schools

by Michael Marland

The core of a radio play, like that of any other form of drama, is the meeting of characters and the clashes of ideas and temperaments that follow: Stan and Eileen, Ruth and Officer Stone, Dumbfounded and Im, etc. But a radio play is an invention in sound only, and the conflict, the characters, the ideas, the fun, and the tensions have to be put over by means of a blank loudspeaker—and nothing else. The producer has just four ingredients: voices, sounds, music and (very important!) silence —no colour, no faces, no views! The producer therefore needs to calculate and control these four ingredients very carefully indeed so that he makes the very best use of them.

You probably know something of the equipment used in the BBC to help the producer control these sounds: acoustically treated soundproof studios, separate glass-windowed control room, numerous microphones, mixers, echo chambers, etc. Is there any hope, then, of making even a reasonable shot at producing these plays with the makeshift equipment of a school and a cast of pupil actors? A very few new schools are being built with modestly but efficiently equipped recording studios. What of the rest? It is difficult, and results will certainly be less than perfectly polished, but effective productions can be done. It is worth remembering that much of the professional equipment is designed and installed simply to save *time*, for staff is limited and expensive and a professional broadcasting organization has to put out a large number of productions. Given time, patience and ingenuity similar results can often be achieved on more modest equipment. Full details of equipment, the operation of tape-recorders, and recording techniques suitable for schools will be found in the books listed below. This note will discuss the application of these to the effective recorded production of the five plays.

The Drama Tape Guide　H. Woodman　(Focal Press)

The Right Way to Tape Record　L. Mallory (Eliot 'Right Way' Books) (Both easy enough for pupils)

The Tape-recorder in the Classroom　(National Foundation for Visual Aids)　(Particularly good on the machine itself)

Teaching with Tape　J. Graham Jones　(Focal Press)

Broadcasting with Children Kenneth Methold (U.L.P.)
(Useful ideas and details on internal broadcast systems, drama,
etc.)

EQUIPMENT

Almost any tape recorder can be used (for fuller information
see *Teaching with Tape*), but for reasonable results a suitable microphone should be added. This is a ribbon microphone which
picks up sound from two directions only. An omni-directional
microphone is not suitable for dramatic work—it does not
select the sounds that are wanted.

The essence of recording a play is control of the sound,
knowing what is being recorded. The second technical requirement, therefore, is some means of 'monitoring', or listening to
the recording *as it is being made*. The simplest way of doing this is
to buy a pair of headphones so that the 'recording engineer' or
'studio manager' can listen to what is going on to the tape, and
adjust the volume according to his judgment. The best way is
to arrange the microphones and performers in one room and
have long leads to the producer and engineers in a separate
sound-proof 'control' room. This allows the monitoring to be
done through a loudspeaker and to be heard by a group of
people. For ease of operation and really effective production, a
'talk-back' system is required, so that by flicking a switch the
producer in the control room can speak through a separate
microphone and be heard by the performers. He can in this way
advise the performers in rehearsal and between sections of the
recording. Ideally there should be a window through which he
can be seen, and cue-lights are helpful so that he can give pre-
cise signals to performers. Some schools have converted store-
rooms, cupboards, or adjoining classrooms as control rooms;
others have built small ($6' \times 6' \times 6'$) 'rooms' out of a double layer
of hardboard with fibre-glass as sound insulation. A control
room like this can be set up in a corner of the school hall. A
temporary but less satisfactory arrangement is to draw the stage
curtains, using the stage as a 'control room' and the hall as a
'studio'.

The third technical requirement is the ability to 'mix' the

various sounds so that, in the dance hall in *The Mating Season*, for instance, the volume of the background music and that of the actors' voices can be carefully controlled. The easiest way, of course, is to play the music on a record-player in the studio, picking the sound up on the actors' microphone, and using the record-player's own volume control to get the levels right. The best way, however, is to connect a *mixer-unit* to the tape-recorder which is being used for recording the play. It is then possible to plug the microphone, a record-player, and other tape-recorders or record-players into the mixer. Each *sound source* can have a separate volume control on the mixer and the exact balance of sounds can be chosen. At the start of *The Day Dumbfounded Got His Pylon*, for instance, the birds might be played on a sound-effects disc on the record-player, the mower might have been specially recorded on tape, and Dumbfounded might be on one microphone and Mrs Skern on another. The engineers can then *mix* the sounds at the right levels.

THE ACTING

A real advantage of sound drama for schools is that the ability to project the voice to the back of the hall that is required for stage productions is not necessary. It is important, though, to choose actors for what their *voices* suggest, not for what they look like. This is best done by auditioning through the monitor loudspeaker, judging suitability by ear alone. Each play requires contrasting voices, and each character requires a voice of the right pitch, quality, and atmosphere. What differences, for instance, should there be between Jack and Stan in *The Mating Season*, or between Officer Stone and Miss Mooney in *She'll Make Trouble?*

Rehearsals are usually best started sitting round a table away from the microphone. The actors need to concentrate first on *clarity*. With only the words to convey meaning, a radio production must above all be clear. They should then consider the *expression*. Think about the characters in *She'll Make Trouble*. A simple example is Officer Stone's remark when she rushes in to announce: 'Lawrence is smashing up her cell' *(page 140, speech 1)*. How should this be said? Some speeches are even more important. One of the first pieces of rebelliousness that we hear from Ruth is her query to the medical orderly (*page 113, speech 16*): 'Have you washed your hands?' If the actress is *too* rude and belligerent, she will make nonsense of the Medical Orderly's humorous agreement (*page 114, speech 1*), and indeed it might lose much of the listener's sympathy for Ruth.

Pauses are most important. When Stan is talking to Eileen at the Dance Hall, for instance, he suddenly looks at his office work in a new light; he sees Eileen's point in the middle of his remark. The actor should hold a good pause, and change his voice to make this clear to the listener (*page 22, speech 17*): 'That's all right, they're only . . . come to think of it, they don't.'

As rehearsals progress, the actors will practise and learn all these points, as well as their positions in relation to the microphone (which will be discussed next). Sound drama acting is usually best with the actors *standing*, and using facial expressions and even some movement of the body to help their voices. They should take great care when turning the pages of copies, as the rustling of paper is easily picked up by the microphone. The aim is to 'live through' the words, so that the listeners will not feel the script is being merely read.

SPACE IN SOUND

The listener will hear all the sounds and all the voices from one point: the loudspeaker. But the listener can be given a sense of space, particularly of the positions of the characters, by how the actors are positioned during the recording, and how they speak to the microphone. This is called the *aural perspective* of the recording. The microphone represents the listener, and in any scene the producer needs to decide where the listener is imagined to be. The actors should then be close or distant to the microphone according to the layout of the imagined scene. In the interview scenes in the Governor's office in *She'll Make Trouble*, for instance, the listener could be imagined to be behind the desk; the Governor will therefore be near to the microphone, and the Officer and prisoners heard from farther away. Similarly, in the café in *Don't Wait For Me* the waitress would be heard coming nearer the microphone, but her voice would never be as close as Lizzie's. There is an interesting and more complicated example of the importance of perspectives in the chapel scene on page 146 of *She'll Make Trouble*. If possible an echo effect should be used here to suggest the large room; try recording this in a gymnasium. Perhaps the first part of this scene is best imagined from the *prisoners'* point of view. In that case, the Governor's voice would be loud, but distant. Tillotson's voice would be fairly close, but shouted just to one side of the microphone. Davis *(page 146, speech 4)* would then whisper very quietly and very close to the microphone. The listener would then imagine himself in amongst the singers.

These perspectives should be decided by the producer and are most important. In particular, he must be consistent within one scene so that the listener is not confused. However, there is nothing very difficult or complicated about arranging them. If, as is best, a ribbon microphone is being used, giving two *live* sides and two *dead* sides as in the diagram, distance can be achieved by simply moving round from the *live* to the *dead* side. The approaching waitress, on page 106, for instance, starts talking on the *dead* side, and gradually moves round.

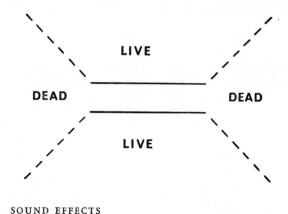

SOUND EFFECTS

You will notice that the scripts do not have very many effects. However, they are important and need to be carefully done. There are three ways of producing the sounds:

1   *Spot Effects* are made in the studio by the Studio Managers
     and recorded at the same time as the actors: Footsteps,
     doors (it is good to have a small free-standing
     door built specially), the clink of handcuffs on page 111
     of *She'll Make Trouble*, the tearing of paper on page 4 of
     The Mating Season.

2   *Effects Records* can be bought (produced by E.M.I.) and
     provide a good range of standard noises, such as the
     bird background on page 88 of *Don't Wait For Me*.

3   *Special Recordings* can easily be made, particularly with a
     portable battery recorder, and would be necessary for
     the background in the pub on page 11 of *The Mating
     Season*, the chip shop on page 100 of *Don't Wait For Me*,
     and probably the prison choir, particularly when it
     goes wrong on page 145 of *She'll Make Trouble*.

In some of these plays music is important as a sound effect,
signposting the scene, and it should not be difficult to choose
the right records for the dance hall and the juke-box in *The
Mating Season*, or the fairground organ in *Don't Wait For Me*.

PUTTING THE PLAY TOGETHER

Each play has an overall shape and rhythm which depends on
the speed of the acting in each scene, the way each starts and
ends, and the sound or silence between scenes. It is easier to
record the play scene by scene, or at least in groups of scenes.
These sections can then be played back, and re-recorded if
necessary. It is, of course, very easy to *cut* the tape and re-join it.
This makes it possible to record some scenes twice, and later to
cut out the least good. It also makes it possible to alter the
length of the gap between scenes after the whole play has been
recorded.

  Of great importance are the fades that start and end most
scenes. The effect of fading-in suggests that life has been going
on before the scene, and that the listener is, as it were, dropping
in. Sometimes the fade-in is on effects (such as the approaching
footsteps on page 117) or dialogue (such as Ada's chat on page
115) which have the effect of *sign-posting* for the listener. The fade
needs to be gradual—not so slow that it gives a misleading air of

mystery, and not so quick that it jerks with an over-dramatic emphasis. Where there are background noises that start the scene and are heard throughout, as in the dance hall on page 21, it is effective to fade up the background quite high to establish it, and then to fade it down and hold it under the dialogue of the scene.

DRAMA IN SOUND

These five plays were invented in their writers' minds as dramas in sound. It was on the radio that they first came to life. Each has a quality that is *aural* and not *visual*: Stan's conversations with Jack, for instance; the memories so effortlessly recalled by the cross-fading in *Don't Wait For Me*; the lunatic conversations in *The Day Dumbfounded Got His Pylon*. All these are creations that can excite the dramatic imaginations of listeners—even on a modest school tape-recorder.